al...... Schoolboy
series

'The humour is infectiously funny,
an... ...re importantly relevant . . . like reading a child's
...ersion of *Hitchhiker's Guide to the Galaxy*.'
Just Imagine

...Out of this world. Endlessly inventive . . .
... tickle and touch children's imaginations.'
Ian Whybrow,
...thor of *Harry and the Bucketful of Dinosaurs*

'Very different. Very funny.'
Jeremy Strong

'Very funny. Very good fun to read.'
Julia Eccleshare, *The Guardian*

'I... a hillarious book and I bet my family would wet
theirself if they read it. Well done!'
...harlotte (Year 6), Doncaster Book Awards

...mething funny and clever on every page . . .
...stute observations on human life in all its
...tionality . . . Asquith's invention never flags.'
Books for Keeps

Ros Asquith started out as a photographer, became a theatre critic for *Time Out*, *City Limits*, and *The Observer* before emerging as a cartoonist. She draws regularly for *The Guardian* and has written and illustrated many books.

Ros lives in London with her jazz critic husband and two sons. She has stroked a tiger, cuddled a wolf, caught an escaped tarantula and juggled in a circus, but mostly prefers reading and eating fudge.

Find out more about Ros at www.rosasquith.co.uk

Explore
alienschoolboy.co.uk

for more
galactic fun and games!

Discover what happened
on Flowkwee's trips to Earth!

Translated from Alien by
Ros Asquith

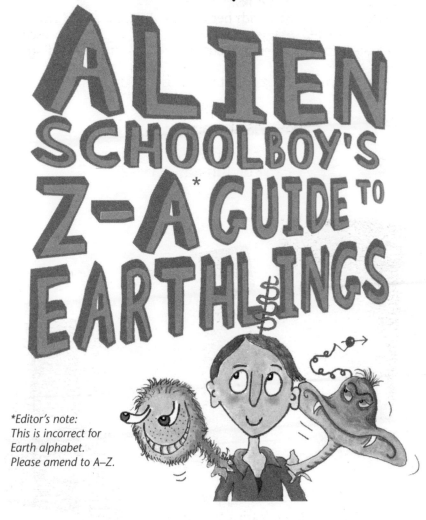

ALIEN
SCHOOLBOY'S
Z-A* GUIDE TO
EARTHLINGS

*Editor's note:
This is incorrect for
Earth alphabet.
Please amend to A–Z.

Piccadilly Press • London

For Jessie and Lola and Lenny
(If you see any spinach,
eat it quickly before a Thregg gets it.)

First published in Great Britain in 2012
by Piccadilly Press Ltd,
5 Castle Road, London NW1 8PR
www.piccadillypress.co.uk

Text and illustrations copyright © Ros Asquith, 2012

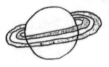

A catalogue record for this book is available
from the British Library

ISBN: 978 1 84812 271 0 (paperback)

1 3 5 7 9 10 8 6 4 2

Printed in the UK by CPI Group (UK), Croydon, CR0 4YY
Cover design by Simon Davis
Cover and interior illustrations by Ros Asquith

Dear Faathings,

Earth is one millionth the size of our planet, Faa.

I have recently made several trips to the small spaceblob known as Earth. The dominant inhabitants, known as 'humans' or 'Earthlings', believe they are intelligent life forms, although they have only one brain each.

I've written this simple guide for those of you who visit Earth, to help you avoid making some of the mistakes I made. Although taking *Vom* will give you the physical appearance of a human, you will have to learn to behave like a human too if you want to 'fit in'. Otherwise you will be treated badly because Earthlings don't like people who are different.

I went to Earth with some of my family on the orders of His Holy Rolypoliness, the Emperor of planet Faa. He wanted us to capture Earthlings and bring them back to Faa so we could use them as slaves. In order to achieve this, I was disguised as an Earth youngling, or 'child'. This guide will therefore be especially useful for those of you who, like me, are disguised as younglings. You will be made to go to school and do all the deplorable things younglings do.

This guide is mainly about the gloomy island called 'Britain' where we stayed. It includes the wet kilty top ('Scotland'), the wet leeky bit to the left ('Wales'), and a drizzly clump in the middle where we were ('England'). However, I made a short trip around the rest of the planet, some of which is drier and more colourful – although the people are univerally drab.

Sadly we did not succeed in our mission. We had no idea how much we would need to Improve Earthlings for them to be of any use to us. Although we built the Improver, a magnificent machine to give Earthlings extra intelligence, heads and obedience, we were unable to bring any specimens home.

While we were there, several species from space – the Threggs, Wiffly Biffly and Squelch – tried to invade. These evil species broke the Interplanetary Codes of Cooperation (which of course applies even to vastly inferior places such as Earth) and so, as Faathings brave and true, we saw it as our duty to help Earthlings fight off these invaders – which we did. However, they will probably try to invade again.

Yours in science,
Flowk

PS: May I apologise for an error in initial translation. The English Earthling alphabet actually runs from A to Z, so the title of this guide is, regrettably, somewhat misleading.

PPS: By the way, my Earthling name is Hoover Bogey Nigel Custard Toilet Hercules Namby Pamby Harmonica Hedgehog Coldplay Bugspray Cro-Magnon Colander Junior. I like it, but Papa told me it would be best if Earthlings just call me 'Nigel'. I advise you to choose a similarly simple name. 'Brian' for a male or 'Pasta' for a female, will do.

What to take to Earth

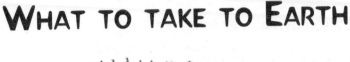

Carry *Vom* at all times. Earthlings have a sad affliction they call 'stress' which affects 97 per cent of them for 94 per cent of the time. Unfortunately it affects us too and causes our Earth disguises to dissolve. A swig of *Vom* will rectify the situation. It's a good idea to keep it in Earthling cola bottles, like we did, to avoid arousing suspicion.

It is also advisable to bring:

* INVISIBLE BEAK MUFFLER

* INTER-SPECIES TRANSLATOR to translate all the human and animal languages on Earth.

* MEMORY BLASTER
Should an Earthling discover you are an alien, you must use this to erase their memory.

* FARTEETA'S AMAZING SHRINKER
Built by my sister, Farteeta, this enables you to shrink Earthlings and other creatures so you can easily bring them home to Faa for experimentation. So far, we have failed to capture any specimens, but other missions are planned.

Farteeta in her hideous human disguise.

☆ WHAT TO EXPECT ON ARRIVAL ☆

You will arrive on Earth in dreadful weather. H_2O (called 'water') will pour from a grey sky. You will be damp and cold for most of your stay.

Earthlings are uglier than anything on our planet and have only one head. Their skins are brownish, pinkish or yellowish – all hideous – and their intelligence is so limited that it will be tempting for you to treat them as pets, or food. Resist if possible, as they have one or two interesting qualities.

☆ NOT TO BE MISSED ☆

I should add that Earthlings do have a few things worth preserving, notably:
- **JOKES**
- **STORIES**

- **CHOCOLATE** and, most importantly,
- **MUSIC** which exists nowhere else in the cosmos.

For this reason alone, I am suggesting that Earth be a 'protected planet' under the Interplanetary Code Zx400000097, paragraph 9&&%@f6p>>0.

☆ EARTHLING DISGUISE ☆

You must disguise yourself as an Earthling otherwise you'll get locked in a prison or zoo.

You are only allowed four limbs. Two 'arms' ending in grippers or 'hands' are used for lifting, carrying and picking beaks (which are packed with glutinous jelly known as 'bogeys'). The two 'legs' are used for walking, skipping, climbing, jumping, hopping or running. Earthlings have no whirlers, tentacles or aerials so are incapable of flying, zooming, whirling or looping. Their limbs are uni-jointed, therefore only bend one way.

Adult Earthling disguise

'Hairstyles'

'Ear'
(Hearing is limited. Earthlings cannot even discern the language of bats.)

'Tie'
or 'necklace' to keep head attached to body

Bogey tissue.

'Beak'
(Unfortunately crammed with 'bogeys' and therefore barely able to smell.)

'Chestbumps'
(For feeding babies and attracting males.)

'Gripper'
(or 'hand'). Only five digits.

Uni-jointed limbs bending at 'knee' (leg) and 'elbow' (arm).

'Skirt'
(Beware - many females wear trousers, making them indistinguishable from males.)

Shoelacy for tying shoe to sock.

'Shoes'
or foot covers.

Once disguised, you will realise how limiting it is to have only two eyeballs. For some bizarre evolutionary reason, these are placed at the front of their single head, so that Earthlings cannot look behind themselves without turning round!

You must dress yourself in 'clothes' which is the only way to keep warm. On Earth, even beds and tables have clothes. NB: Male and female clothes can be different.

Now my alphabet begins. I hope I have included the main things which will confuse you, although it is tempting to write so much more. For instance, about glue, egg cups, marbles or any of the many curious things that Earthlings think they need.

Aaaargh

What Earthlings say when they are cross or frightened or have made a mistake. Easily confused with 'Aaaah' which is what they say when they are pleased.

It's important to get this right, or you can find yourself pretending to snuggle up happily to an Earthling who has just been shot in their one and only head, or calling an ambulance for an Earthling who is cuddling its pet.

ADULTS

Adult Earthlings who can be teachers, parents, dictators, film stars and murderers. They are also known as 'grown ups'.

This is because they have grown UP, and so are taller than younglings, but they have not grown noticeably wiser.

Adult accessories
(Can be worn by younglings, but less common.)

'Hats'
If you see an Earthling with a peculiarly shaped head, do not be frightened - it is likely they are simply wearing a 'hat'. These are for decoration and protection from rain and bird poo-poo.

'Face vegetable' or 'beard', worn by gods, giants, goblins and rabbits*. Do not wear if disguised as female Earthling or youngling.

'Spectators' or 'glasses'.

*Editor's note: Sorry, that should be 'rabbis'.

Earthlings believe they are superior to younglings, and some of them *can* do simple sums and read a few words, but they prefer 'shopping', watching TV, throwing dishes about, shouting at cars or telling younglings to 'SHUSH'.

Adults do not always follow their own advice. For instance, they say to younglings:

1) Do not fight.

2) Be polite.

3) Share your toys.

But

1) They fight wars all over Earth.

2) They are the most impolite species it has been my displeasure to encounter. In cars, they hoot. In shops, they shout. They never send younglings 'Thank you letters' when younglings make them 'birthday cards'.

3) They don't share toys (TVs, houses, husbands or cars).

⭐ **TIP:** You must pretend adults know more than you do, especially teachers.

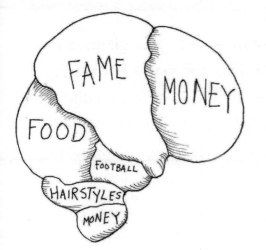

I have conducted an analysis of the average adult Earthling brain (see left). Earthlings <u>do</u> have other thoughts, but they represent a tiny percentage.

Here is just one of the four brains of a baby Faathing - the simplest brain available on Faa. An illustration of all four adult Faathing brains would be so big it would take up 36 volumes of this book.

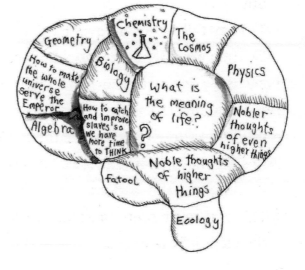

ALIENS

Earthlings oddly do not worry about alien invaders much. That is partly because they are so busy worrying about money and hairstyles but also because they are unaware that we Faathings have already saved them three times from destruction by Threggs, Wiffly Biffly and Squelch. However, there are powerful rumours on the Interplanet that aliens are massing for a fourth invasion under the leadership of the evil Keith, King of Threggs, and that another species, possibly

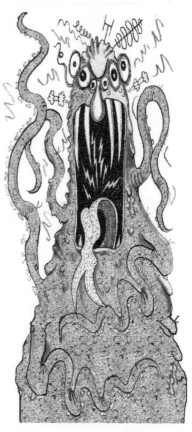

Keith,
Lord of the Loonyverse
and King of Threggs

more deadly than Keith himself, is joining them.

Remember, therefore, that Threggs are desperate for spinach, so don't go anywhere near a greengrocer (vegetable 'shop'); Wiffly Biffly are violently attracted to cardboard, so keep as little of that near you as possible; and Squelch need wetness, so are constantly a danger if you are forced to stay in little Britain where it rains every day.

A cardboard-loving, laughter-hating Wiffly Biffly

Mandy, Queen of the Squelch

However, all three can be defeated. Threggs are terrified by Earth's greatest invention, music. Wiffly Biffly are horrified by custard and 'jokes' and Squelch are defeated by 'stories'.

ALLERGIES

These decorate Earthlings' eyeballs red and make them sneeze bogey explosions. Some Earthlings are allergic to cow juice, some to dry grass called hay fever, some to insects, some to pets, some to school and some cannot eat anything except pizza. What weeds they are.

On Faa of course, we have the kind of technology that created the Improver, so every time any Faathing gets slightly out of balance with the environment – which is all allergies are – they can be Improved in a flash.

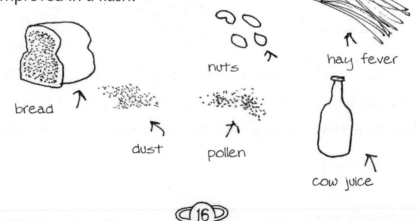

bread

nuts

hay fever

dust

pollen

cow juice

I have come to like some Earthlings, despite how moronic and humongously feeble they are, so I have every hope we might Improve them until allergies are no more.

Earthlings do like having things wrong with them to moan about, however, so don't hold your breath. (It is very easy to hold your breath, but this is an Earthling 'saying'. You need to understand their banter if you want to pass yourself off as an Earthling.)

⭐ **TIP:** If offered Earthling cardigans to wear, or asked to pick up an Earthling baby, say you are allergic to them.

ALPHABET

The Earth language English has only 26 measly letters, a few languages like Chinese have several thousand letters, but none have the two million that we have. This means that Earthlings do not have enough words to express many feelings or ideas, and some words confusingly mean different things. Here are just a few examples to watch out for:

'Tear' means crying H_2O from eyeballs and also ripping something apart. One kind of tear can result from another.

'Mouse' means a charming scampering little rodent (we had lots of them in our Earth dwelling and I loved to chat to them at night) but it can also mean a computer control.

'Nail' is an unpleasant horn-like claw covering human digits, but also a sharp tack for sticking furnitures together.

'Rock' is a combination of Earth minerals but also a gentle swinging motion mamas do with babies. Rocking a baby does *not* mean throwing minerals at it! Rock is also an excellent form of Earthlings' greatest invention 'music'.

'Bow' is a simple three letter word but it can mean the front of a water transport, *or* a ribbon for female hairstyles and presents, *or* a wooden stick attached to the hairstyle

of a horse for playing musical furnitures, *or* a weapon to shoot 'arrows', *or* to bend forward at the waist.

Younglings take ages learning letters but they still can't spell correctly. I originally spelt 'Learner' as LOLOGNYRRH.

L is 'L'.

'OLO' is 'er' as in colonel.

'GN' is 'n' as in gnat.

'YRRH' is 'er' as in myrrh.

Why can't they just spell things the way the letters sound in their alphabet? Which should therefore be spelt 'alferbit'.

No wonder, with all these problems, Earthlings are such slow lolognhyrrhs.

TIP: You *must* make spelling mistakes in your homework – all Earth younglings do.

ARMIES

'Leggies' is a baby word for Earth legs, but 'armies' is a collection of warriors. This is because 'arms' confusingly means Earthling upper limbs, but also weapons.

Earthlings would love to have as many extenders and whirlers as us, but they can only grow two on their tops ('arms') and two on their bottoms ('legs'). To make up for this, they build extra arms from metal, and pretend they're important by using them to blow bits off each other. If we could Improve Earthlings to grow more arms of their own, they might be more peaceful.

In a popular game, 'the arms race', countries compete to make 'guns' and 'bombs' to explode each other. Even Threggs don't do this! On most civilised planets, there is one army in case of interplanetary invasion and many have no armies at all, yet there are thousands on Earth.

'Drawings' or 'sculptures' represent real or imagined things. (Imagination – a form of lying – is common on Earth.)

Younglings hurl messy colours at paper or make art from glue and the cartons of unhatched hens that parents place proudly in their dwellings. Grown-up artists make similar art, which is placed in museums and galleries, where Earthlings must be very quiet and not tell anyone they don't like it.

Younglings visit museums and galleries on 'school trips' with 'worksheets' instructing them to find vegetables hiding in the paintings. This is tiring for teachers, who must say, 'No, that is not an onion wearing a crown. It is a king!' and 'You must not draw a beard on that nice portrait of a lady'.

Their colours are a disappointing mixture of red, yellow and blue. They have no infra-red, ultra-violet, *oravalooom* or *valanium*. To our eyeballs, all their colours are dull.

FOR ART: AGAINST ART:

Artist's hat or 'berry'.

Artist's face vegetable or 'moose tash'.

Empty pocket.

Look of gloomy boredom.

Artists say:
'Nobody understands me.'
'Can you lend me a fiver?'
'Van Gogh never sold a painting.'

Spectators say:
'My five-year-old could do better.'
'This looks like dog poo.'

I quite enjoyed doing art and so have illustrated this guide using drawings. My little doodles are far superior to those produced by anyone else at school.

baBieS

Earthling babies are howling, screaming, *footling* little organisms that make only meaningless sounds like 'Waaaa', 'Goo-goo', 'Bleaaahh' and 'Ick'. Their lower limbs are formed from a jelly that does not support their piffling weight, and they spray body fluids in all directions if not tightly wrapped in plastic wrappers. They are kept in three kinds of cages – playpens, buggies or cots – and are fed cow juice from their mummy's chest bumps.

They keep trying to walk, despite falling over thousands of times, whereas we can zoom and loop when we are just a few hours old.

TIP: Stay away from them at all costs, or you might be asked to change their wrappings.

Earthling females must carry portable pockets full of face-painting kits, bogey tissues and hairstyle scrubbers. Younglings must carry school pouches with gum, 'packedlunch', farting cushions and forged letters saying they have a tummy ache and must spend all day eating ice cream as they are too tired for lessons. Bags are for leaving on buses and losing things in.

I have looked inside these 'handbags'.
They also contain money, hairstyle smoothers,
scrubbers and pluckers, keys and fluff (a vital
possession, but I am still uncertain whether
it is a medicine or a lucky charm).

Commonly found in females' handbags

'Lipstick' - unfortunately it does not stick lips together to prevent the constant yacketty yacking of females.

'Mascara' - goo to turn eyeball lashes into pretty spiders.

'Powder' - gives skin a flaky appearance. A mild improvement.

← Hairstyle scrubber.

← Hairstyle smoother.

← 'Eyeball liner' - to outline eyeball so it is easier to see.

BALLET

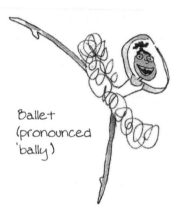

Strange Earthling ritual which we believe is some kind of ongoing anti-gravity experiment. Even the most practised Earthling investigators are unable to jump to their own height, let alone eight or ten times their vertical dimension like we can.

Ballet (pronounced 'bally')

These experiments seem to be taken very seriously on Earth, however. Many Earthlings gather to watch them, and the participants wear protective clothing in case of accidents – often looking like 'meringues' (puddings made of unhatched baby hens) pretending to be 'swans' (half 'bird', half 'giraffe'), twirling on the ends of their 'toes'. You must be polite about this ritual if you want some girls to like you.

BATS

Earth creatures that fly and sleep upside down just as we do. Their high-pitched squeals are inaudible to most Earthlings but I am delighted to report they are plotting to take over Earth, helped by ants and charming water mammals called dolphins. I should say I hung out with a bat one night who wasn't very optimistic about this plan, which they've apparently all been squeaking about for thousands of years. He complained he'd never met an ant who could think for itself in a crisis, and that dolphins secretly like Earthlings.

Anyway, it's a good idea. Earth will be better and humans will be happier as they can laze around picking their beaks. Obviously, upside-down sleeping is better for brains.

⭐ **TIP:** Do not let anyone see you communicating with bats. They will say you are 'bats', which means mad.

Bees

This is how humans spell the noise of bees

Bzzzz zz ezz zzzzzzzzzzz

Adorable fuzzy flyers with a proboscis like our own, that they use as we do, to pollinate flowering vegetables. Earthlings are unable to do this. Earth's food supply depends on brave little bees but Earthlings poison the vegetables with insecticides which kill the noble bees! The poor mama bee, or 'queen' has to lay 2,000 eggs every day, just to keep the numbers up. The Queen of England, however, only has to lay four eggs as no one sprays her with insecticide.

BICYCLE *

Wheeled creature with a human head, which speedily weaves between great vehicles to frighten them.

Editor's note: Flowkwee has forgotten that this is, in fact, an excellent Earth vehicle which does not pollute the planet's atmosphere as 'cars' do. Please correct.

BIRTHDAY

On Earth, you get presents every year just for being alive. Of course, Earthlings' poor vision, lack of coordination, stupidity, terrible diet and aggressive tendencies make their lives quite unpredictable and dangerous, so perhaps this is why they're regularly rewarded for survival. While we Faathings have an annual party when our elders reach 100 to celebrate their achievements, Earthlings' achievements are only celebrated when they are dead, at a 'funeral'. Yet

Earth babies of ONE year old, who are pooing on the carpet, are given presents and 'cake' (a flaming cookery made from unhatched

baby hens, cow juice and flowers) and told how clever they are. Younglings must go to 'birthday parties' to play unpleasant games which make everyone cry, especially the mamas. Party guests will demand presents called 'partybags', even though it is not their birthday.

⭐ **TIP:** If you *are* forced to give an Earthling party, do not do as Mama did, which was to ask adults to play 'Pass the parcel'.

⭐ **TIP:** If it is someone's birthday be sure to say 'Happy birthday' and 'Congratulations' and 'What did you get?' as if you mean it.

Baby ignoring its birthday.

BOO

An insult, but by just adding more Earth letters it can mean many different things: 'Boob' which means mistake (or lady's chest bump), or 'Boohoo' (crying), or 'Book', or 'Boom' (explosion), or 'Boon' (good thing) or 'Boot' (large foot cover), or 'Booze' (alcohol). This sort of carelessness with language leads to a great deal of misunderstanding on Earth.

Earthlings do read books as we do, although be warned – theirs are as likely to be about made-up events as true ones!

We read a very interesting book at school about a princess who kisses a frog who is then transformed into a handsome prince. I wanted to see this and so I kissed a real frog and was disappointed when nothing happened. Then Farteeta planted some beans in the garden expecting them to grow into the beanstalk she had read about, which  would lead to a land of giants. We were both very shocked when we found out that neither of these stories were true.

At first I was cross that we had been lied to, but now I think their made-up stories are quite exciting. Their information books, on the other tentacle, are very boring, containing nothing that you don't already know.

⭐ **TIP:** The Squelch can be defeated by stories. If you come across a Squelch, just start telling a story, or say the titles of stories or even, 'Once upon a time', which is how many Earthling stories begin.

Boredom

This is when Earthlings fall asleep because they are not interested in what they're doing. If this is a reason to fall asleep, it's odd that they are ever awake at all, considering how much time many of them devote to curtains, shopping, weather, TV . . . I am falling asleep just writing this.

☆ **TIP:** If you need an adult to think you are awake, paint realistic looking eyeballs on your eyelids.

Looks a bit like this, or this

Your Earth disguise means you are going to have to wear one of these (not at the bottom, but on the middle of your body at the back, which is why it is often referred to as a 'behind'.)

Considering they are quite important items for Earthlings (permitting them to sit without sliding to the floor, keeping their lower limbs attached to their body, improving accuracy in their ghastly 'toilet' activities, etc) it is surprising they find bottoms so funny. I have failed to discover why. Bottoms do sometimes speak, but Earthlings always pretend not to hear them, which is rather disrespectful.

Luckily, unlike Earthlings, you will not have to use your bottom for poo-poos. Ignore it and it will ignore you.

Youngling boys (male) and girls (female) are educated together on Earth!!!!! In fact, they are considered more or less equal! Females are even allowed to be teachers, bus pilots and even the King of England (called Queen Syllabub the Second). Mama and Farteeta think this is a good thing.

It is very difficult to tell which Earthlings are male and which are female. I thought my closest friend Susan was a fine fellow till I discovered she was a girl. You can sometimes tell by their names, toys, hairstyles and clothes, but not always.

I made a few unfortunate mistakes, wearing clothes that for some reason only females wear – like violet welly boots covered in pink hearts, and a flowery swimming costume.

If Earthlings are so sure males and females are 'equal', I am not sure why boys can't wear these things, or nice dresses.

BULLIES

People who hurt other people intentionally. This doesn't just mean hurting their bodies – their feelings can be hurt too. For instance, all Earthlings are smelly and spotty but their feelings are hurt if you tell them this. 'Sticks and stones may break my bones but words can never hurt me,' is one of those Earth 'sayings' that no one believes.

On Earth, bullies are everywhere. When younglings are bullied by other younglings, teachers tell them to say, 'Stop it, I do not like what you are doing.' This would not work with Colin Snell, who once tried to push my Earth head inside a toilet. I was so disgusted, I nearly vaporised him, but instead I unfurled three minimal extenders and flipped *him* head first into the toilet. It wasn't my fault that whoever had been in there before hadn't flushed it.

⭐ **TIP:** Do not do as I did and risk revealing your alien identity. It's better to poison the bully's packed lunch.

BUT (do not confuse with BUTT)

If an Earthling says to you, 'No offence, but . . .' or 'Not to be rude or anything, but . . .' you can be sure they are going to say something rude.

Earthlings like slipping this little word in just after they've said something that seems to be agreeing with you. It is an example of how their primitive language encourages disputes and wars. I have also discovered that on that large Earthling continent called America this word is spelt with two 't's, but then it means 'bottom'.

TIP: If you hear the word 'but', close your ear trumpets and run away before you inadvertently extend your posterior tentacles and strangle the offending Earthling.

BUTTONS

Impossible fasteners for clothing. Five Earth digits are not enough to do up even one of them. They are usually attached to 'jackets', 'coats' and 'trousers'.

TIP: Wear items fastened with velcro or zips. Or a jumper. Avoid ugly cardigans if at all possible.

Jumpers are better than cardigans. Wear one with an Earthling hero on it, not a teddy, like I did.

'Jumper' - a rather disappointing clothe. It does not jump but merely hangs about.

CARDBOARD

Prolific item used to make packets, boxes and, I am sorry to say, rolls for disgusting 'toilet paper'. It is best avoided as the Wiffly Biffly, the second nastiest baddies in the universe, are so attracted to cardboard that they want to marry it. If you see small, fluffy pink creatures saying these words, pelt them with custard or tell them jokes to make them go away.

'Here we come,
the Wiffly Biffly,
Here we come so
softly, swiftly.
We can never
be ignored
in our quest
for our adored
CARDBOARD.'

CARTWHEELS

To do a cartwheel, an Earthling spins on grippers with shoes in the air. Everyone claps and says 'wicked' (meaning 'good').

TIP: Say, 'Well done, what a spiffing cartwheel'. Resist the temptation to perform 2,000 of these simple rotations followed by a quadruple somersault and posterior tentacle extension back flip. People will say you are showing off.

chocolate

Earthling 'sweetie' made of cocoa solids. We don't eat Earth foods but my friend Roddy gave me some chocolate. Not wishing to be rude, I popped it in my mouth intending to spit it out later, but it melted before I had a chance to. Delicious!

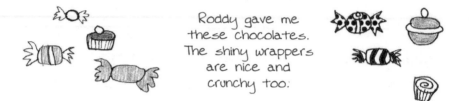

Roddy gave me these chocolates. The shiny wrappers are nice and crunchy too.

Why do Earthlings eat pets like chickens and hot dogs when they could eat chocolate all the time? It is one of the few pleasant things found on this dreary spaceblob, Earth.

To see my Earth face eat the chocolate, move the page slowly towards you until your beak touches the planet.

CINEMA

Dark room where younglings crackle popcorn while adults go, 'Shush!'. A screen shows 'films' which are moving images that Earthlings enjoy more than their real lives. Some of these images are '3D' but they are nothing like our holograms or twelfth dimensional videotropes.

'Film stars' are some of the most powerful people on Earth, yet all they do is pretend to be people who don't really exist. People who *do* really exist copy the ways film stars dress and talk, except they don't think they look as good and so become unhappy with themselves. How can any creature with only one head and four limbs be so envied?

CIRCUS

Entertainment that is usually in a 'tent' – a big dwelling made of cloth. Earthlings perform tricks that a baby Faathing could do before he learns to loop. They think it is brilliant to walk along string or turn a simple triple somersault. 'Clowns' squirt liquids at each other, walk on stilts and their trousers fall off, making adults laugh and younglings cry.

⭐ **TIP:** Clap your grippers together and say 'Ooooh', even at these simple stunts.

⭐ **TIP:** Should your disguise slip, explain you are from a circus. When Mama painted her lips and cheeks bright red and her eyeballs green to be like Earthling mamas, everyone thought she was a circus clown.

Earthlings have no fur or even scales, so they warm themselves with tubes and flaps called 'clothes'. This at least means we see less of their unpleasant skin. They even have 'underclothes', though I haven't discovered why yet.

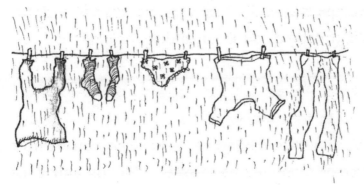

This is called a washing line.
Earthlings like to hang clothes in the rain.

Clothes are impossible to put on. Just figuring out where 'pants' go took forever. I tried putting an arm and a leg through the two smaller holes, but I had to walk around bent double. Then I put my head and one arm through, but it pulled the one miserable head over at such an angle that I couldn't see and kept bumping into things. I tried pulling them down over my head with the eyeballs looking through the holes, but they covered the beak, which the primitive human respiratory apparatus uses for breathing, so I thought I was going to die. It got worse from there. I put the shirt on the wrong way round, and I spent hours trying to do the buttons up at the back.

I could go on . . . What a waste of time! You could visit the Hyades for a game of pong ping, download a dictionary or two at the Infinite Knowledge Base by the Timeless Labyrinth's *koma* bar, and even drop by Aqua Orbius 9 for a quick swim in the time it takes to 'get dressed'.

☆ **TIP:** Take a month or two to practise getting dressed before your Earth visit.

Chest protector – females only.

TIP: If a male, do not wear a chest protector ('bra') or frilly underpants. If you do, you will get the laughing noise. Don't ask me why. Remind your papa not to wear an Earth suit in pink as adult males choose only black, grey or dark brown for almost all of their clothing.

On Earth, clothes are supposed to 'say' something about the wearer.

I have never been to Mexico.

I am short.

I am cool.

I cannot cook.

Leeve me alone weeth my art.

My mum made me wear this.

47

COMMON COLD

Not a description of Earth temperature but an illness which plagues Earthlings. Luckily, we cannot catch it, but you have to be careful of Earthlings who have, because they become even more unpleasant to be around than usual – alarmingly similar to our mortal enemies the Squelch in their sinister wetness, ill temper and crazed mission to engulf their surroundings in a tide of green goo. Earthlings' eyeballs water and their one throat becomes encrusted with yellow puss*. Their beaks erupt in a hail of flying bogies (a 'sneeze'), spreading the germs to other Earthlings. Adults say, 'Use a handkerchief' (tissue covered in bogies) which just spreads germs to even more Earthlings. It is polite to congratulate someone when they sneeze, by saying 'Bless you'.

My sister, Farteeta, discovered which germs cause the common cold and asked them for the cure. So far, they

*Editor's note: Sorry, that should be 'pus', otherwise they would be swallowing mysterious yellow cats.

48

have been sneezing too much for her to understand everything they say, but she thinks the cure is as follows:

* one shredded banana skin
* a tablespoon of egg yolk
* a teaspoon of earth
* four wombats' legs, minced
* *fluit* juice (from Faa and not to be confused with Earth 'fruit juice')
* lava (2.25 litres)
* ground moon rock from Omega Centauri (the globular cluster in the Centaurus constellation).

A cold germ

The potion must be heated to 8,000 degrees centigrade, stirred thoroughly and applied to the beak three times a day for a year, after which the Earthling will be cured.

Apparently Earthling pharmaceutical companies would offer Farteeta loads of money for it if it worked, which means nothing to us as we can print money whenever we want.

NB: You can also catch a 'cough'. The cure is to hold a small furry animal (e.g. a mouse) in your mouth for an hour.

Computers

Computers are infinitely better than one Earth brain, but they are making Earthlings even more stupid. Now Earthlings have computers, they don't bother to learn anything any more – they just 'Google' things they don't know. I know we sometimes use Booglewoogleooglenoodlepoodleapplestrudel on our Interplanet, but then we have the whole knowledge of the universe at our disposal.

⭐ **TIP:** If someone asks you a question, don't answer immediately – make sure you pretend to 'Google' it on your 'phone' or 'laptop' first.

The first Earth keyboard was invented by a visitor from planet Qwertyuiop, which explains the weird top line of letters that Earthlings still use today.

'Countries' all
have different
flags that they
wave to show
that they are
the best.

Weirdly, Earthlings divide their puny planet up into hundreds of different 'countries'. They do not know how many countries there are, but it is between 168 and 250, depending on who is doing the counting.

Amazingly, countries also have different 'money' and 'laws' and between them there are over 6,000 languages spoken, which means very few Earthlings can understand each other.

Countries seem to cause most of Earth's problems. A few are very rich and the many poor ones don't think that's fair. If the poor ones complain, the rich ones say they're troublemakers. If the rich ones want to help, the poor ones think it's a trick. Leaders in the different countries argue all the time about who deserves what and who's better than who. Earthlings kill each other a lot over these and many other things. It is very sad. If we had more time, we might be able to Improve their brains and stop them. But I fear they are so far behind Intergalactic evolution it may be too late.

'Country' also means landscapes without thousands of dwellings piled on top of each other. 'Countryside' consists of vegetables like grass, corn-on-the-cob and hay fever, and animals like sheeps, alligators and wallabies. The countryside is divided into rectangles by fences. In lots of places you cannot walk on countryside without asking. Country people live in tractors, farmyards and fields of pooey mud.

As a schoolchild you will have to know what the latest 'craze' is. It might be rotating hoops on hips, hopping in circles, yoyos on strings or collecting blobs or miniature figures to swap or fight with. Younglings are happy to learn about hundreds of countries, armies, special powers and characters for their crazes but they hate learning anything at all about Earth's real history and geography.

I can think of much better crazes anyway, such as collecting holograms of former dictators from the Ninth Quadratic Wars, seeing who can build a hyperdrive engine from an incomplete circuit diagram fastest, collecting *flonkblatters* which can stand on all their heads at once, blow stuff out of their beaks in an interesting range of colours, perform brain surgery on each other, and a quontillion other things. I will start one of these crazes on my next visit.

CREATURES

Earthlings believe they are superior to other creatures. How odd. Ants, for instance, are far cleverer. An ant's brain accounts for six per cent of its bodyweight. If that percentage were applied to Earthlings, their heads would be three times their actual size. Delightful flies have superb vision, more like our own, but Earthlings hate them as well as charming mice and adorable headlice.

Perhaps Earthlings are just jealous of these nimble, plucky little creatures, whereas they are terrified of noble lions and dinosaurs. Yet they admire aggressive bears, even making them into cuddly toys for their babies.

I have now conversed with cows, sheeps, pigs, dolphins, lions, camels, penguins, spiders and other species to find many of them have excellent ideas although some are a trifle dull. Cows, for instance, are only interested in their digestion and talk about it to each other all the time. 'Mooo,' means 'My stomachs are feeling very well today, thank you.' 'Mwaaaahh,' however, means, 'I knew that grass

I hear that on Faa there are five moons to jump over.

was out of date,
I wish I hadn't eaten it.'
But then they *are* clever
enough to digest grass in
the first place. If humans
could do this, there would
be no starvation.

Birds produce their own music, like humans.

I have not yet spoken to any birds, who invented music, but I hope to on my next trip.

Earthlings have much to learn from animals, but many species are becoming extinct because they keep killing them.

CUSTARD

Always carry tins of this sticky
yellow 'pudding' as it keeps
the Wiffly Biffly at bay.

Smoothy CUSTARD

DANCE

Strange Earthling gymnastic activity used as a pleasure-signifying ritual. It is usually performed by two or more Earthlings, though sometimes only by one if under the influence of the oddly popular brain-vaporiser 'alcohol'.

Dancing often takes place at social functions such as 'parties', and requires Earthlings to wave their extenders randomly about, bump into furnitures and each other, and sometimes fall down.

Dancing is performed, though often very inaccurately, to that wonderful Earthling creation music. It seems a very disrespectful and ignorant way to behave while music is in the middle of speaking.

DAY

An Earth day is divided into 'day' and 'night'. Days are slightly lighter, when the Earth faces the sun, although the sun is seldom visible behind the soggy clouds. Watching this single weedy fireball rise in the morning is one of the best sights on Earth – although it is nothing compared to the dance of our six suns as they rise over the mountains of Vadoodlemofflybunx, of course. However, hardly any Earthlings see it as they are all lazing in bed.

A typical youngling's day is spent as follows:

Adult shouts, 'Get up'. Repeats six times.

Adult pulls youngling out of box or 'bed'.

Adult shouts, 'Get dressed'. Repeats six times.

Youngling puts on tubes and flaps.

Youngling made to scrub beak, eyeballs, chewing blades and hairstyle.

Youngling fed scorched bread with glue and unhatched baby hen.

Youngling thrown into vehicle and taken to queue in road.

Youngling shoved out of vehicle into prison called 'school'.

Teacher shouts, 'You are late'.

Lessons all day with shouting in playgound and lunch of pig sticks and cake.

More vehicle queuing and shouting.

Adult shouts, 'No TV till you've done your homework'.

Youngling eats tea of hen nuggets and biscuits.

Youngling lies, 'I have done homework'.

Youngling glued to TV.

Youngling glued to computer.

Adult shouts, 'Go to bed'. Repeats six times.

Youngling undoes tubes and flaps and is forced to scrub body and chewing blades before beddy-byes.

DENTIST

We don't have any type of doctor on Faa now, of course, but we've certainly never had a doctor just for chewing blades. Younglings' chewing blades can fall out because of sweeties and fizzy drinks so they must open their mouths while the dentist rummages around inside with saws and pokers. If the youngling stays quiet they get a 'smiley face' sticker.

Many centuries ago on Faa, I once heard, there was a desire for less pointy chewing blades among our people. The beautiful Nemisene race had

Youngling opens mouth while dentist rummages inside with 'chisels' and 'saws'.

just been discovered and liberated from slavery in the Third Quadratic War. They had almost circular, gleaming silver chewing blades and some stupid Faathings wanted our head-doctors to make them copies. But it turned out the Nemisenes found our pointy blades very attractive, inter-species relationships developed, and we soon forgot the whole idea.

☆ **TIP:** If your Earth disguise has yellowish chewing blades, wear a blueish clothe.

DESERT

Comfortably warm sandy plains decorated with charming spiky vegetables – not to be confused with 'desserts', which are puddings eaten at the end of meals.

Small lumps of compressed coal worn by female kings (called 'queens') or film stars. 'Miners' burrow deep into the ground to dig them up, and give them to rich people in return for a slice of bread.

Diamonds and other Earth 'jewels' are very similar to the glass used to cover portholes and have nothing like the radiance of the necklaces worn by our beloved Emperor's favourite wife, but there's a 'song' (a type of music) called 'Diamonds are a Girl's Best Friend' which confirms that Earthlings prefer these 'toys' to each other.

TIP: Earthling mummies sometimes wear diamond circles on their grippers. Do say, 'How very sparkling and prettily beautiful, you must be very rich.' Do not say, 'Why do you love a small lump of compressed coal?'.

DINOSAURS

Delightful-looking creatures, especially the cuddly Tyrannosaurus Rex, which is the same size as many of our pets. I hoped to see some on my journey round Earth with Susan, but when I mentioned it she laughed and told me how little I know. This is strange coming from someone who does not know that for every non-zero complex number z there exist two numbers!

My friend Roddy has lots of model dinosaurs and *he* agreed it would be fun to find some. They *must* be more intelligent than Earthlings.

I do so hope to meet this adorable fellow on my next Earth visit.

An Earthling film, *Jurassic Park*, tried to turn dinosaurs into film stars but as with most Earthling plans, fundamental errors – such as allowing the dinosaurs to eat their fellow actors, etc – resulted in distrust and failure.

Earthlings who mend ill Earthlings. We used to need them on Faa back in the Fourth Quadratic period before we had cured all illnesses, but feeble Earthlings need doctors constantly, even for having a dripping beak or a splinter.

 TIP: If you want to skip school, tell your teacher you have a headache (remember, never use in plural). Then you will be allowed to go home. Do not roll around in pretend agony, as they may call a doctor who will take out his 'stethoscope' and hear all your hearts beating.

DUCKS

Yellow quackers that must be floated at 'bathtime'.

DUST

Fine powder covering everything on Earth and made mainly from human skin, which Earthlings are careless enough to shed wherever they go. Earthlings seem to be fond of dust because they often carefully move it from place to place by stroking it with a pet cloth called a 'duster'. This causes them to sneeze bogey explosions but apparently they gain some satisfaction from having looked after the dust. At least we assume this is their motive, because the quantity of dust continues to increase.

earth

Just 4,600 million years ago, Earth was a ball of molten rock. Life started about 3,500 million years ago, and human life began just two measly million years ago, which explains why Earthlings are still so very simple-minded.

Earth is one of eight tiny planets in the flimsy solar system at the wrong end of the universe (Milky Way galaxy, number 5000007).

Earthlings think all their air is oxygen, but it's only 21 per cent oxygen and 78 per cent nitrogen. Oxygen, which we enjoy from time to time on Faa, is essential for life on Earth, but it may disappear because Earthlings have no idea how to look after their planet and then they will be vaporised in a cloud of poisonous gases.

Earth landscape consists of mainly seas and oceans – which are masses of H_2O which Earthlings think are huge but which are similar in size to our puddles, and mountains – which are small slopes no higher than eight kilometres at the most.

Earthlings amuse themselves by trying to climb these mountains, from which they sadly often fall to their deaths. But if you map the air currents, mountains are easily climbable with a couple of flips of the rear extender and a few zooms. Earthlings also like trying to dive to the bottom of their oceans. They have not yet succeeded in going to the very deepest part yet, but I intend to as I hear there are some exceedingly interesting civilisations down there.

Earthling expressions are very limited as their single head can only show one emotion at a time. They change their expressions mainly by changing the position of the furry lines above their eyeballs and turning their mouths up or down at the end.

It is worth practising the limited range of human expressions using your Earth face. This should only take you a few milliseconds at the most.

The range of Earthling expressions are limited as their one head only expresses one emotion at a time. These diagrams are based on my Earth teacher, Miss Barn.

Angry	Furious	Pleased	Happy
Unhappy	Annoyed	Amused	Ecstatic
Depressed	Cross	Thoughtful	Patient
Upset	Hungry	Quizzical	Relieved
Exasperated	Sad	Exhausted	Hungry
Beginning of	Exhausted	End of the	Wistful
school day		school day	

FAIRIES

Insects with human heads which can fly. When I mentioned to Susan that I would like to meet some, she said I was 'away with the fairies.'

'No, I am not,' I replied crossly, 'that is the problem. I would like to go away with them because they obviously share some of my powers, but I can't go away with them because I can't find any!'

Roddy said he thought he knew where fairies lived and that he would show me some one day. I can't wait. Susan laughed and said surely he didn't believe in fairy stories. This means she thinks fairies are just stories; creatures Earthlings would like to believe are real but aren't. But Earthlings know so little about what's really happening around them, I don't see why fairies shouldn't exist just like all the other little flying animals on their planet.

FAMILIES

We have several mummies and daddies, but Earthlings have only one of each parent and some have only a mummy *or* a daddy. Perhaps Earthlings have chosen to live like this because they only have one head.

Imagine what it's like: when we are cross with one of our mummies we can always go and find another. The Earth family is hopeless, because how can just one or two adults look after the primitive Earthling youngling? These poor small 'families' are crammed inside horrid little dwellings so they are usually playing the games called shouting, sighing and grumbling.

Earthling parents come in three packages:

Cross,

Very cross, and

Furious.

Things you don't hear Earthling adults say:

No, you can't have any Brussels sprouts until you've finished ALL your chocolate cake!

Why not stay up all night watching TV?

Why of course, dear, you can have all the sweeties you like.

Oh, have you broken my computer again? I'll see if I can find you another one that you can kick safely.

Often you will hear a mama Earthling saying, 'What planet are you from?' to her youngling.

It should be perfectly obvious to her that the infant is from Earth, the only planet in the universe where younglings are allowed to choose which ice cream flavour they want for ten whole Earth minutes while a long queue forms behind them – and surely also the only planet where younglings can pretend they have a tummy ache to avoid education!

Other adults in a 'family' include knobbly shouting uncles, spindly crying aunties and crinkly grump-parents. Hardly anyone has great-great-grump-parents like we do. Susan didn't believe me when I told her that my fourth great-great-great-great-grumpma was 206 and that she could still fly and zoom like a youngster.

Poor Earthlings live with so few people. But then again, with only one head, they cannot have four conversations at the same time as we can. You must constantly be aware of how limited they are in this respect.

However, they do have the advantage of having fewer siblings than we do. It is uncommon for there to be more than six younglings in a family and often there is only one. That said, we might be arguing with 60 of our brothers and sisters with all four heads at once and still make less noise than a couple of sisters down on Earth who like pulling each other's hairstyles.

TIP: It is worth bearing in mind the strong possibility that Earthlings do feel affection for their family members just as we do. I have seen some evidence of this. If a youngling is crying because her mummy has run away with the postman, do not say (as Mama did), 'Oh but you must have lots of other mummies.' I also noticed that when Susan was captured by the Wiffly Biffly, her mummy cried H_2O.

FLATTERY

Important Earthling custom where you tell untruths to make someone feel 'good about themselves'.

Here are some helpful examples you might like to try.

To your teacher: 'You are so clever, knowing your times tables,' or 'Thank you for not shouting today, your voice sounds as sweet as a muffin.'

To someone's mummy: 'What nice, bouncy chest bumps you have – they could feed millions of babies at once,' or 'I think your diet is working – your elephant legs are more like sticks today.'

To someone's daddy: 'Your baldy patch on your hairstyle is getting smaller. Well done!'

FLUFF

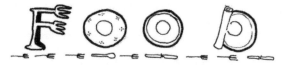

Vital item that Earthlings always keep close by, in their pockets or under their beds. It is either thought to be lucky, or it is a medicine. Much of its composition is dust, which Earthlings also carefully cultivate.

FOOD

Poor Earthlings must eat three meals a day to keep alive. They do not enjoy their food as we do and must boil or burn it so it is without taste or smell.

I hate to shock you in case you haven't read my other books, but Earthlings cook and eat creatures, including pets. They boil baby pigs ('sausages'), scorch cows ('burgers'),

roast little canines ('hot dogs'), and wreck sea creatures (fish'n'chips) by burning them in ovens.

'Recipes' are rules to follow before you are allowed to eat.

Earthling TV, newspapers and politicians worry about younglings overeating and getting trapped in revolving doors or undereating and being sucked down plugholes. Every day different foods are 'healthy' or 'unhealthy'.

Foolish adult Earthlings are always hoping to look more 'beautiful' by following 'diets' – instructions about how to eat a slice of lettuce instead of a cow. Females read magazines to tell them how to be thin. But, lacking science, they don't understand that diets *don't work* because as soon as they eat normally again, Earthlings expand like balloons.

Don't laugh when they say they dream of being beautiful. Although they are the ugliest species in all the galaxies, they DO NOT KNOW IT!

There are four main food types to nourish younglings:

Hen nugget
(chopped hen, burnt and covered in crumbs.)

Unhatched baby hen.

Chip
(potato vegetable dug from Earth, shredded and scorched.)

Ice cream
(frozen cow juice)

Although Earth parents know fruits and vegetables are good for their younglings, they prefer to feed them in the following way:

Breakfast: Bowl of cardboard and cow juice. (Try to avoid even saying that word that ends in 'board'. . . It attracts the Wiffly Biffly. They can look cute, but they are the second most evil species in the multiverse.)

Lunch: At school. Either packedlunch, or a choice of pig sticks, pizza (cow juice and dough cake) or 'bakedbeans' (vegetables in hard shells called 'tin cans') with birthday cake and 'custard' after. (Good for getting rid of Wiffly Biffly.)

Supper: Hen nuggets and crisps, followed by biscuits and jam.

Thank *Klong* we Faathings can get all our nutrients from a single pill each week and enjoy plucking the fresh fruitlets and vegetables that grow everywhere on Faa and placing them in one of our four mouths. Earthlings' single mouths can only discern five flavours: sweet, sour, bitter, salty or savoury instead of the hundreds of different flavours our four mouths can sense.

But, I have tasted nothing better anywhere than Earth's amazing chocolate. I did try to bring some back to Faa but am ashamed to say that Farteeta and I finished it all before arriving home.

⭐ **TIP:** You will not be able to digest Earth food (except delicious chocolate) but must learn to prepare it for Earthlings. Mama's favourites are roast potato jelly, mustard bums and cupcakes.

I used to think cupcakes looked like this.

But now I know they look like this.

⭐ **TIP:** Don't mistake the 'oven' for the 'fridge' as Mama did. Our Earth guests did not like the cold pink 'meat' and Mama had to serve them cabbage biscuits instead.

FOOTBALL

Favourite sport of English Earthlings, especially males. I have heard it originally started with the kicking of an enemy's head, rather than a ball, but I have my doubts. Firstly, an adult Earthling's head weighs around 4.32 kg, whereas a football weighs only 0.3968 kg. Also, heads don't roll well. But from the way some 'football fans' behave, I think they would prefer to use a head.

Football is similar to our own traditional game of *fatool*, originally devised by the legendary warrior race of Goonathons on the low-gravity planet Reff in the minus-quadrupleth century. But Earthlings play with only one ball because they are without springs, whizzers or buzzers, and can kick with only one foot at a time.

To score a goal, you must kick the ball in between two posts. An Earth goal is so wide that even a newborn *fluit* could

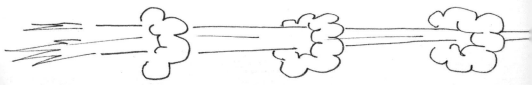

kick a ball into it. And that's all you have to do! So it's a little different to *fatool*'s rules of kicking a dense formation of protons down a heavily defended galaxy-wide tube ringed by hyper-magnets, and your score is the megatonnage of the resulting nuclear reaction to the nearest squillion.

When I first played football at school, I stuck out a posterior extender and doubled its length, kicked the ball, calculated its trajectory and descent, skimmed horizontally to meet it 'on the volley' as Earthlings say, and shot it into the goal off the crossbar before anyone knew what was happening. It's lucky I was not playing against a team of flies, whose superior vision would have spotted these speedy movements.

☆ **TIP:** Be warned – if you score a goal, Earthlings will jump on you and hit you. This is a sign that they are happy, but it is quite frightening.

☆ **TIP:** Remember to score only five or six goals per match, not hundreds.

FRIENDS

On Faa, we like everyone almost equally unless the Emperor advises us not to, although we like our families best. Earthlings have to 'make' friends and often want lots of them whereas we are happy with no special friends, or just one. Female younglings must have a 'best friend' while males prefer to be part of a pack. At my Earth school I 'made friends' with Susan because she was nice to me, and with Roddy because he flaps his arms and collects sweetie wrappers and pencils and likes dinosaurs. No one else 'liked' him, but that is because Earthlings do not like anyone who is different.

You will miss your Faathing friend and family because however close you get to an Earthling, you will never have the wide range of thought transference or conversation you have at home. Earthlings do not even have basic telepathy, so their friendship is naturally very limited. This is proved by the strange habit they have of making friends using their internet with people they have never met.

⭐ **TIP:** To make friends, you need glue, ribbon, scissors, an electric motor and six metres of humanoid 'skin'. To befriend a real Earthling, offer kettles of whisky to adults and sweeties to younglings.

FURNITURES

You will be confused by how many furnitures Earthlings need in their houses: beds for sleeping on, cubes and rectangles for sitting on, curtains for keeping portholes warm, carpets for keeping floors warm, tables for covering with crumbs and papers, cupboards for filling with combs and socks and buckets and rope and onions and celery and cardigans – I could go on but it is tedious.

When we first arrived on Earth, Mama was trying to work one of the new kitchen furnitures that's for washing things. She had put the cups and saucers in it. I stood staring through the little window on the front of it while all the things inside whirled round and round, smashing into bits. 'Maybe the machine sticks them all together again once they're nice and clean,' Mama said, but it didn't. We later discovered the whirly washer was for clothes, not plates. So here's a quick guide to the most common furnitures.

Oven: For burning pig sticks and vegetables.

Fridge: For cooling cow juice, dead hens and leaves.

Freezer: For freezing dead hens and leaves and for keeping snowballs and ice cream in.

Dishwasher: For cleaning china discs and metal prongs. Humans must eat off these 'plates' using the prongs and small swords. They spend more time cleaning them than they do eating their food.

Washing machine: For tubes and flaps and also clothing for beds and portholes – do not confuse with dishwasher.

Kitchen sink: For filling with dirty dishes and fluff.

Basin: For scrubbing hands, head and chewing blades.

Toilet: (See *Toilet*.)

Bath: For immersing whole body (remove clothing first). You must have a sea creature called 'sponge', a slippy toy called 'soap' and a yellow quacker called 'duck'.

Shower: Rain machine for rinsing skin.

TV and computer: Primitive versions of our holograms and Interplanet, almost always in just two dimensions.

Earthlings love to play computer games, 'board games' and sport.

The game on Earth that intrigued me most, because it has no element of luck, is a modest-looking board game called 'chess'. It uses the appalling Earthling enthusiasm for armies and war, but you win it by using your brains, not by blowing things up. However, Earthlings take such a long time deciding on moves that a simple *flaaark* could make in a nanosecond that sometimes you wish something would blow up just to stop you falling asleep. You will want to play, but beware! You will be very good at it and beat Earth champions in a few seconds. They don't like that.

If disguised as a youngling, you will have to take part in games at school sports days involving eggy spoons, sacky legs and falling in heaps.

Common Earth games

Basketball
Throw ball into basket.

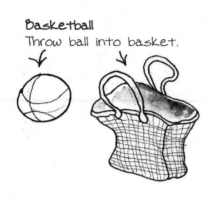

Rugby
Roll egg of ostrich in mud.

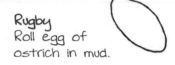

Ice skating
Falling over on frozen H_2O.

Crick-it
Wave bat about to hit other players with cement sphere. NB - not <u>this</u> bat.

Golf
Walk about carrying handbag of 'clubs'.

Tennis
Hit ball at ground or into 'net'. Earthlings must call each other 'love'.

Every four years adults do Olympics, which is running, jumping, swimming and spending money. All the world's countries join in to see who is the best by getting the most gold medals. To us, these activities are tragic, being the kind of thing our babies can achieve at one week old. Their 'high jump' for instance, is a measly 2.45 metres

The best Earthlings get given golden teacups in some competitions.

and their fastest runner can only sprint 100 metres in 9.58 Earth seconds. The strongest humans can only lift 263 kilos!

⭐ **TIP:** You must pretend to be excited and go 'Oooh' and 'Ahhhh' and cheer at Earth's simple games.

⭐ **TIP:** The temptation to show off your powers at school sports day may be overwhelming but do not be tempted to whirl, loop or zoom. Remember to fall over in sacky legs and drop your unhatched hen babies in eggy spoon. On no account start flying.

GARDENS

Those who cannot own or enjoy some 'countryside' make 'gardens' full of flowering vegetables and bird feeders. Ancient Earthlings stumble around gardens in floppy hats waving digging prongs. Earthlings who are good at making things grow are described as having 'green fingers'. I have tried hard to find this species, but without success.

☆ **TIP:** If in England, never make fun of someone's garden, even if it is all nettles, broken washing machines and old pizza cartons.

GENIUS

Your greatest challenge on Earth is *not* to be called a genius. It is almost impossible to pretend to be such a duffer as Earthlings. I was called a genius on my first day when I calculated the square root of -34,876 and even when I got full marks in a spelling test. Farteeta got in trouble at playgroup when she demonstrated some basic local geometry (working out the trajectory of a 'marble run' which she'd assembled in two nanoseconds to make the marbles whizz over the sandpit, loop round the dressing-up corner and drop straight into the teacher's pocket). She made it worse by asking why humans thought they were cleverer than flies.

Nearly all Earthlings who are called geniuses were in fact space visitors from the mildly clever planet Zargon. Zargonites visited Earth over the last few centuries in an attempt to Improve Earthlings in the most peaceful way they could, by inventing, writing, painting and so on. It would be rude to mention this to Earthlings, as they are proud of the few clever people they think they have created.

Zargons themselves have only limited intelligence (roughly similar to an Earthling IQ of 180), and they were further limited by taking their mission very seriously. They pretended to be 'born' and 'grow up' on Earth. Zargonites even pretended to 'die' so they could return home. Luckily Earth life spans are short. I will tell you about just a few.

Archimedes ran naked out of his bath shouting 'EUREKA!' (which is Zargon for 'There is a spider in the bath' but is luckily similar to the Greek word for 'I've got it!').

Jane Austen was a writer of stories who gently poked fun at Earthlings. People thought she died aged 41 but she hated England so much she just fled home.

Copernicus was the first to convince any Earthlings that Earth is not the centre of the universe. (Yes, up until then they did believe that, and some of them still do.)

Leonardo Da Vinci was a scientist, artist and inventor who tried to get Earthlings to imagine submarines and aeroplanes until he finally gave up. His most famous painting, 'The Mona Lisa', was of his mum, who came to visit for a year from Zargon. She never could quite learn how to smile in the correct Earthling way and so Earthlings are always intrigued by her strange expression.

Charles Darwin told Earthlings they were descended from apes and had evolved over many centuries. Some Earthlings still don't believe this.

Thomas Edison invented the electric light which meant that Earthlings could do things in the evenings. Until then, they had just lazed about with little flames called candles.

Albert Einstein was clever even for a Zargon and therefore exceptional for an Earthling. His physics led to modern Earth lasers, TV, computers and space travel, but other Earthlings tragically warped his ideas to invent nuclear bombs. This upset Einstein, who campaigned for peace all his Earth life. Like so many Zargons, he tried to do good, but Earth has a way of turning good ideas bad.

Mahatma Gandhi campaigned against war all his life, trying to show Earthlings that peace was better. He pretended to be dead but is in fact still alive on Zargon.

Isaac Newton was a physicist and mathematician who taught Earthlings about the three standard laws of motion and explained to them about gravity. (No, they didn't understand it until he told them!)

William Shakespeare wrote plays (where Earthlings pretend a story for other Earthlings to watch). Because

Earth languages are so basic, he had to invent lots of words, like 'critic', 'gloomy' and 'lonely', which show how he really felt about this planet. Earthlings still use many of his words today.

BUT, one thing Earthlings can be proud of – Zargons did not know about music. All Earthling musical geniuses are genuine Earthlings!

GHOSTS

Transparent humans, dressed in bedclothes, who often carry their heads under their arms and go, 'Woooo, wooo'. Younglings dress as ghosts to frighten adults at the annual festival called Hallo Ian.

GIANTS

Big hairies as tall as our Faa selves who live up beanstalks and say, 'Fi-fi-fo-fum'. They are becoming extinct like so many nice Earth species.

GLOBAL WARMING

Earth may feel freezing to you and me, but the planet's temperature has increased by 0.8 degrees centigrade in the last 60 years and there is more CO_2 and methane than at any time during the last 800,000 years. So sea levels rise, deserts expand, glaciers melt, weather gets worse and more species die. But Earthlings continue to squabble and burn up fossil fuels, which produce more harmful gases.

Earthlings know that wind, wave and solar energy are

kinder to the atmosphere, but they have not bothered to find a way to make them power all the contraptions they think they need. They cannot fly, so I understand their desire for transport. They have no fur or scales, so I understand their need for heat. But if only they could be happy solving mathematical problems and considering the meaning of life and the universe as we are, they wouldn't need to use so much energy.

We must teach Earthlings how to properly use nuclear fusion, which has solved energy problems on most planets. Otherwise Earthlings will pursue their own dangerous form of nuclear power which releases poisons and you can't clean it up if it goes wrong. Earthlings make 'jokes' about this, as they do about most things they're frightened of. They laugh about how living next to a reactor may make a person grow six legs or glow in the dark. These seem like perfectly normal qualities to me, so I don't see what's funny about them. However, if a nuclear reactor blows up, it could destroy their planet. I will never understand Earth 'humour'.

Many Earthlings believe that their planet and everything on it was created by a bearded being called God who lives in the Earth sky.

Earthlings believe God will look after them but they also believe he sends floods and hurricanes to punish them, as they do not fully understand the science of their (admittedly dreadful) weather.

Many Earthlings believe in different versions of this 'creator'. The ones I've heard about so far are Jehovah, Allah, Zeus, Father Christmas, the Pope, Buddha, Lady Gaga and Queen Syllabub the Second of England.

God is actually invisible but some versions of him are elephants and some are little fat men. Earthlings spend a lot of time praying to their elephants and fatties and others and build much better houses for them than they do for their poor people. These houses are called churches, mosques, temples and synagogues and are decorated with angels or mosaics or big colourful portholes. I don't know why God needs so many houses, even though many Earthlings have nowhere to live.

 TIP: You may be tempted to ask Earthlings why, if they were designed by God, he did it so badly? Be careful who you ask, though, because some Earthlings will see this as very rude.

Gorgeous creatures with frizzy hairstyles who can turn Earthlings into stone with a glance. If you meet one, and don't want this to happen, you must show it a mirror so it

turns itself to stone.
Perhaps this is why
Earthlings are so
attached to
mirrors. I have not
found a gorgon yet, but I know
there must be one living near the
zoo, because I found many of her
snakey hairstyle clippings living there.

Weapons that kill, with bullets, a bit like the *fargleschnufters* that our security services carry. Imagine what it would be like if we were all allowed to have one like many Earthlings are. Instead of disagreeing with one head at a time and then discussing it with two or three heads before expanding into a full-blown argument using all four heads simultaneously, we could just blow each other to pieces with a *fargleschnufter*! This is what Earthlings in many countries are allowed to do.

Younglings love 'toy' guns and computer games about killing which prepare them to grow up and shoot real people. When I asked Roddy about this, he just flapped his arms and said guns were fun, so I think this will take a few centuries to change, by which time Earth will  either have overheated or all the guns and bombs Earthlings keep making will have finally blown the place to bits.

I hope you get a chance to visit before that happens.

HAIRSTYLES

Tufts of fur on top of the head which Earthlings worship as they cannot grow fur elsewhere. Earthlings visit hair houses where hairstyles are dressed, frizzed, burnt and turned different colours, usually browns or blacks or yellows. Teenagers try pinks and greens but parents say, 'Change that NOW'.

Hairstyles can be helpful in distinguishing males from females as females often wear their hairstyles long with decorations or ribbons and males often wear theirs short. But this is not reliable and must be used with other clues.

Hairstyles are also the homes of charming headlice, which hop happily from head to head, so you can easily collect some by rubbing your Earth head against your schoolfriends' hairstyles. You can chat to them at night if you are lonely and with luck they will lay lovely eggs called 'nits'.

Hairstyles to look out for

Mow Hican
(teenagers,
footballers)

Bird's Nest
(younglings, beggars)

Purrm
(grandmas,
teachers)

Baldicoot
(babies,
grandpas)

Girl
(but <u>could</u>
be boy.
Check name and
clothing)

Boy
(but <u>could</u>
be girl.
Check name
and clothing)

TIP: Stand outside a hair house to watch females going in looking hopeful and coming out looking sad. Susan says it's because they want to look like 'film stars'.

HALLO IAN[*]

An event that occurs once every Earth year on October 31. I was told it was called 'Hallo Ian' by a six-year-old Earthling I met during one of these strange festivals. He was dressed in a black binliner and had a plastic sword painted with tomato ketchup stuck through his head – or maybe I should say 'skull', since he was wearing a mask painted to look like one.

If you want to take part, you must have a fat orange vegetable called a 'pumpkin' dressed up as a person. Younglings pretend to be 'witches' or 'ghosts' and bang on doors shouting, 'Trickortreat'. Grown-ups open the doors and give the little savages sweeties. Sometimes adults give smaller orange vegetables called 'tangerines' and the younglings say, 'Yuck', even though these vegetables are much better for their chewing blades.

I am very fond of the Earth sweetie called 'chocolate,' so I

*Editor's note: Flowkwee has misheard 'Halloween'. Please correct.

am going to join my new school friends in their Hallo Ian if I visit Earth again.

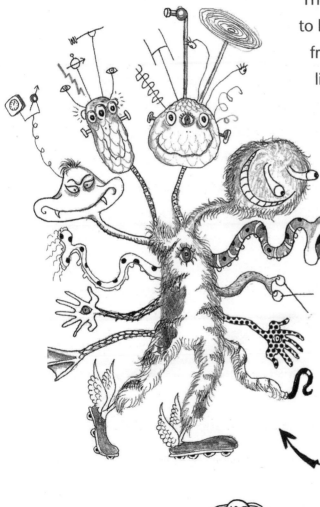

They say the point is to look scary, but my friends look like bin liners in bandages. Since Earthlings find anything that's different scary, I am going to take off my Earthling disguise and go as myself. That should get us lots of sweeties.

Me, without my horrible Earth disguise.

HARRY POTTER

Famous Earth boy who has many of the powers that we Faathings possess. Earthlings call his powers 'magic' whereas we know they are simple science. He has defeated many evil creatures, just as we have, but when I said I would dearly love to meet him, Susan just giggled and said I was 'sweet'. I like it when Susan does that, but am still not sure how to contact Mr Potter on my next visit.

A 'wand' which Earthlings use for 'magic'.
The boy Potter uses much better ones.

HOLIDAYS

A period of time when Earthlings don't have to go to school or work. Younglings like holidays a lot because they hate learning.

Earthlings must constantly cheer themselves up by going 'on holiday' which means leaving behind their usual miserable routines for a short time and having a different miserable routine somewhere else. Unfortunately, being unable to hop to other planets like us, they are stuck on Earth. They travel to different places in their own country or, if they are rich enough, travel to different countries.

They usually like to go somewhere they can see the sun, often beside the big puddles of H_2O. Earthlings lie on sand hoping to make their skin go a darker grey. Instead, it goes scarlet and peels off in flakes. NB: Our Earth disguises, being made of brand new skin, are endangered by this process.

Younglings like to run into freezing cold oceans and cry, then roll in sand till they cry some more. They build 'sand castles' which the sea knocks down so they cry. They get ice creams, which fall in the sand, so they cry.

Adults sit around saying that the holiday is too hot, too cold or too expensive.

'Camping' is a cruel holiday ritual where families live in flimsy cloths called 'tents'. The point is for the tent to blow away and everyone to drown. If the tent fails to blow away, Earthlings try to burn it up

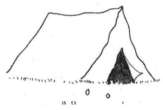

with a 'camp fire'. If that doesn't work, they burn baby pigs called sausages and pretend to enjoy eating them instead.

⭐ **TIP:** If forced to do sand-lying or 'sun bathing' be sure to wear clothes and a balaclava (scratchy headcover made of sheeps which covers head)*.

⭐ **TIP:** If invited to 'go camping', refuse.

*Editor's note: Balaclavas are often worn by Earth criminals, so choose something else. Not a plastic bag – you could suffocate.

Holidays are for:

Getting bitten by insects.

Burying brothers in sand.

Enjoying a swim.

Enjoying the sunshine.

There are lots of different kinds of Earth dwellings. Many Earthlings are crammed into tiny huts smaller than a car's home, whereas others live alone in large castles. Boringly, their dwellings are almost always rectangular. I don't know why Earth architects don't use all the 3D shapes available to them, like the polyhedron or the

Less 'civilised' homes are often a more interesting round shape.

octagon, even if they don't have the infinite variety we do. Portholes and doors are usually rectangles too. Even their 'rooms' are rectangles.

I lived in a measly house constructed of different 'rooms'. Earthlings love their rooms and are always dressing and undressing them, giving them presents of new furnitures –

carpets and rugs to keep floors warm, cushions for chairs to cuddle and curtains to cover up portholes.

Rooms are all dressed in patterns and packed full of things Earthlings think they need. They are even given names, like pets. Here are the rules for what you must do in them.

Kitchens: For arguing, clattering, burning and consuming food. Kitchens have lots of 'drawers' and 'cupboards' because kettles and whiskers and crumbs and fluff and swords and prongs and dear little bugs and charming mice all need homes. Earthlings love kitchens more than physics or even film stars. They often Improve and 'extend' them, perhaps because *they* long to be Improved and have extenders of their own.

Toilet: Happily, as we absorb every molecule of our food, you will have no need of 'the smallest room'. Often this room is combined with the bathroom. You can pretend the 'toilet' is just a sitting furniture or 'chair'.

Bathroom: Earthlings stand outside this room and shout, 'ARE YOU GOING TO BE IN THERE ALL DAY?' It is for splashing, singing, immersing bodies in H_2O and washing hairstyles, chewing blades, fingernails and beaks. You must dry your Earth skin with a trowel which you should leave on the floor, next to the soap and yesterday's 'underpants'. I do not trust Earth soap to actually clean anything, since it was originally made from animal fats and ash, although it may be cleaner nowadays.

Bedroom: Younglings are forced to spend all night in these rooms, lying down on hard boxes called beds, which wear clothing called pillers and doovays. You will miss sleeping under the stars, hanging upside down from an *urquflurble*, chatting to it as you drift into sweet dreams before waking to watch our six suns rise.

Some younglings are forced to sleep in layered beds or 'bunks'. If you get one, you must shout, 'I want the top one. IT'S NOT FAIR!'

Most pictures show tidy bedrooms but most youngling bedrooms look like Earth warzones.

Living room: For saying, 'No shoes on the sofa!' and 'Where's the remote?'. Often contains lovely music machines and pretty pictures of tarantulas or scorpions and TVs for being glued to.

While there is a living room, there is, I am glad to report, no dying room. You can choose which room to die in.

Rooms are linked by tunnels and, if the dwelling has more than one level, Earthlings must climb ladders. (Being unable to loop or fly, Earthlings need steps for everything, even for getting on and off their own 'pavements'.)

TIP: Whichever country you visit, you should live in a dwelling. If you move around as we like to do, they will call you a 'gypsy', and hate you.

TIP: If someone lives in a flat or a bungalow, it does not mean they are flat or a low bungler, it means they live in a one-level dwelling.

homework

If posing as an Earthling schoolchild, you will be set 'homework' by your teacher, who says it will help you 'meet deadlines, keep promises and work hard'. Well, it's *fnooks* to that. Homework encourages idleness and dishonesty because everyone makes excuses for not doing it and younglings forge doctors' letters saying they are too ill to do it.

☆ **TIP:** Earth handwriting is a disgrace. Be sure to learn how to do it badly before your visit.

☆ **TIP:** Learn to spell atrociously too. Or atroshussly.

This is a very good book. It is 732 pages long. Each page has 368 words. So the whole book is 269376 words. I have read all of them. It begins very well, with a capital letter and ends excellently with a full stop. It has an average of 8 sentences and 2 paragraphs on each page which makes a total of 5856 sentences and 1464 paragraphs.

HOSPITALS

Many Earthling younglings are 'born' in these buildings and unhealthy ones go here to be mended. They cannot grow new body parts as we can and their knowledge of anatomy is so poor that even if they could perform a transplant on themselves, half of them wouldn't know where to put the new organ. They only have one heart, pair of lungs, etc, so they are very vulnerable.

Hospitals in England are free, but in some countries Earthlings must pay so poor people get sicker and die sooner than rich people. Susan's mum says one day you will have to be a million air to stay alive in England.

⭐ **TIP:** Resist the temptation to cure Earthlings. If you reveal your identity as an alien, you'll be locked up in an experimental zoo.

Ice Cream

Blobs of frozen cow juice flavoured to taste like Earth vegetables. It is very useful – younglings cannot resist it and so you can lure them into your Improver with it.

INTELLIGENCE

Intelligence on Faa and on Earth are very different things. We take it for granted that from when we are younglings we can calculate a rocket entry trajectory in our heads in milliseconds, speak hundreds of the multiverse's languages and memorise the contents of great libraries. Earthlings are proud of an intelligence that can do none of these things. They do not realise they are the dimwits of their galaxy.

So how can we, one of the most noble and brilliant species in the multiverse, help the poor clods?

Personally, I believe their best chance for having a happy life is to enter our marvellous Improver and come to live a life of duty and devotion to our beloved Emperor on Faa. HAIL TO THE EMPEROR.

But Susan has told me she doesn't want to be Improved and she doesn't think other Earthlings do either.

So what hope is there for them?

Please send me your ideas to include in my next Guide.

 TIP: Despite the above, Earthlings love to be told they are clever, even for performing simple animal tasks like having babies. Praise them at every opportunity.

J.A.C.K

Popular Earth boy who climbs beanstalks, kills giants, jumps nimbly over candlesticks and goes up hills with a girl called Jill 'tofetchapailofwater'.

He is also called Jack of Hearts, Jack O'Lantern, Jack of all Trades, Jack-in-the-box, Jack Spratt, Jack Frost and Jacket.

Crown

← Pail of H₂O

Beanstalk

JOBS

Adult Earthlings must go to work so that they can earn money to pay for food, fluff, buttons, water, air and holidays. Jobs that we would think are important on Faa, like helping ancient folk or cleaning dwellings, are not paid much money on Earth, but film stars and bankers are paid lots.

Other important Earth jobs are footballers, superheroes and 'celebrities' who have very white chewing blades and bouncy chest bumps. Mama's heads were turned by 'fame' and she wanted to stay on Earth and be a film star. Surprisingly (since the work looks very easy), it is difficult to get these jobs, though millions of people all over the planet dream of doing them.

☆ **TIP:** Learn the names of celebrities, footballers and superheroes so you can talk at length to other Earthlings.

Ha HA Ha Ha Ha Ho Ho Ho Ho Ko Heh Heh Ha HA

'Laughing' is an unpleasant, creaking, Earthling reaction to something called a 'joke'. We have examined the mechanics of jokes extensively because they are obviously significant aspects of Earthling communication. As far as we can tell, jokes seem to be largely about space/time miscalculations – like falling over, treading in dog poo-poos and bumping into solid objects. It is sad to say but male younglings particularly enjoy jokes about burping, farting and toilets. They are also amused by the word 'pants'. Why?

Sometimes jokes are even sillier and take the form of questions. So if someone asks you, 'What do you get if you cross a kangaroo and a sheep?', they will think you odd if you give the true answer (an interesting combination of a domesticated ruminant mammal and a wild marsupial from the family *macropodidae*). Instead, reply that you do not know. They will then say, 'A woolly jumper'. You must then say, 'Ha ha ha.'

TIP: Learn one or two jokes before you arrive on Earth. They are useful for 'fitting in'.

TIP: I have also discovered the most significant use for jokes – that they can be used to defeat the dreaded Wiffly Biffly, fluffy predators of the multiverse. This has of course led me to consider there's possibly more to jokes than meets your eighth eyeball.

Ha ha!

Ha ha!

Ha ha!

KEYS

All Earth dwellings in the 'civilised' world have locks to secure their doors and portholes, and so prevent burglars robbing them of furnitures, paperclips, money or fluff. Keys undo locks. Younglings are rarely given them in case they lose them, which is odd as adults are always losing their keys. Your observational memory and X-ray vision will be useful to Earthlings when they do lose them and become very distressed about it.

KISS

Kissing is a disgusting-looking wet splattery thing that Earthlings do with their mouths to show they like each

other. So far, I have only kissed an Earth frog – which is a
pleasant green amphibian
reminding me of my third
mummy – hoping it would
turn into a prince.
(It didn't.) Some poor
younglings have to be
kissed every night by their
mamas or papas.
Adult film stars kiss a lot in

Earth 'films', which is even more unpleasant because
these sucking and slurping activities are portrayed very
close up. They should issue a warning before these
moments, so you can pass the time calculating the
number of cells in an Earth chicken or something until it's
over. (Actually, that wouldn't take long enough, they go
on kissing for ages. Maybe calculate the number of cells
in an Earth elephant.)

LANGUAGES

Earth has over 6,000 different human languages although Earthlings rarely bother to learn any except the one around them. They believe other creatures only make a few

Sorry, I don't speak Crocodile.

sounds but many species chat away more interestingly than humans. Use your inter-species translator so that you can enjoy conversations with creatures that Earthlings believe to be inferior. Sheeps, for instance, love to use words beginning with 'B' like, 'Bold beast Bertie belched, bumped into broken branches, lost balance, bounced on his bum over the bank by the brook, bashing into bristly briars and blackberry bushes by the bog, bruising his back and his big bottom black and blue.' (To Earthling ears this sounds like, 'Baa baa baa'.)

Before my first visit I took the trouble to learn Latin, an Earthling language spoken by 'The Romans', a conquering race with emperors like us. Romans used to be fine people but they have turned into Italians who are lazy duffers just like everyone else on Earth. I was told that Latin was good to learn but nobody speaks Latin now, and you just get the laughing noise if you try to. Learning Latin was a whole hour wasted.

In our school
we can speak
62 langauges.

This sign is up in the school I visited. Can you spot the mistake?

LAW & ORDER

Different countries on Earth have different rules and punishments. On Faa, you are vaporised just for disagreeing with the Emperor, but Earthlings in charge are not always allowed to do this. Earth teachers, for example, are not allowed to vaporise pupils, although a lot of them would like to.

The rules are also not the same for every person. Rich Earthlings can steal fortunes with no punishment, whereas poor Earthlings can go to prison for stealing fluff.

☆ **TIP:** If you see crime on Earth, call the 'police' (the Earthling security service), don't try to solve it. You must respect its laws, however foolish, or a judge wearing a dress and a long grey hairstyle will put you in prison.

☆ **TIP:** Disguise your *Vom* in a cola bottle or Earthlings will think it's an illegal substance and might arrest you.

Losing (STUFF)

Earthling custom which must be done every day. Things younglings lose are: socks, money, homework. Adults lose keys, cars, spectators, umbrellas and minds.

When Earthlings find something, they say, 'It's always in the last place you look.' Are there really Earthlings who go on looking after they've found something?

Susan's granny lost four umbrellas last year.

Roddy lost seven socks last week. Roddy loses everything.

MAMMALS

All human Earthlings are mammals, but not many of them know they are vertebrate, endothermic animals with three middle ear bones. Mammals range in size from the 30-millimetre bumble bee bat to the 33-metre blue whale which many younglings believe is a fish. Earthling scientists have counted 5,676 mammal species, on the planet, although Zargons have identified 1,482 more.

Oddly, although humans guzzle other mammals, they seldom eat each other.

TIP: Remember that Earthlings do not like to be reminded they are mammals like apes. They like to think they are more important.

MANNERS

These are Earthling rules about how people should talk and behave together, so they don't have their 'feelings' hurt or begin hitting each other. Since Earthling feelings are always being hurt, and they strike each other a lot, manners are clearly not a very good system. This may be because Earthlings actually find their manners just as confusing as we do, but if you don't try to get them right, they can get you into a lot of trouble.

One word you must use often is 'please', which you must say whenever you want something. Teachers like to ask, 'What is the p-word?' which often makes the class laugh because one of them whispers, 'Peeee'. (I have no idea why they find this amusing.)

When I was first asked this question I said, 'I am not sure Miss Barn, but perhaps it is "policeman" or "perpendicular"

or "polyhedron"?' which made the laughing noise increase until I had to swig some *Vom* to stop my heads and suckers shooting out.

You must also say 'thank you' when anyone gives you anything, even if you didn't ask for it and don't want it.

Manners vary from country to country, like so many things on Earth. Mama had heard that Earthlings like to rub their beaks together when they meet. She attempted to rub beaks with our next-door neighbour and he ran away so fast he unfortunately fell down the trap door into our 'basement'. Perhaps it isn't something they do in England.

Papa discovered that when adult Earthlings greet each other they should 'shake hands'. I extended my right gripper to connect with the right hand of Mama's new 'friend', Maureen. My first attempt was too hard and made Maureen squeak, my second lifted her into the air and my third was an unintentional full-length extension which pushed her straight through a porthole. Luckily the porthole was wide open and on the ground floor.

Sample remarks that are 'good manners':

'Good mid-day, nice Mr Postman, sir, thank you for giving me this lovely leaflet about pizza deliveries.'

'Excuse me, lady madam teacher miss, but I am exceedingly interested in the study of the human mind. Would you care to share your extensive knowledge with me?'

'Hello dear kindly attractively dressed neighbour! Welcome to our humble home. May we offer you a kettle of gin? A slice of Marmite pie? A broccoli meringue or two?'

'Good aftermorning, handsome strong and lively Mr sir lord police officer. I trust you are having great success in your easy work of spotting burglars and catching them in your net. I would be happy to assist in any way possible so that you can go home to take an early bath.'

TIP: Practise 'shaking hands' and remember to say 'please', 'thank you', 'sorry' and 'excuse me' even when you do not mean it.

How to impress an Earthling teacher with good manners

Stand up when she enters the room and greet her politely.

Offer to help in the classroom.

*Only say this if your teacher's name is Miss Barn.

MaRRiage

Do not be alarmed if you pass one of God's houses and observe big-hatted humans pelting each other with scraps of paper and aiming weapons with flashing lights at each other. It is a quite safe 'wedding' where Earthlings spend fortunes on clothes they wear only once and invite relations to visit who they will never see again. The paper is 'confetti' and the weapons are peaceful 'cameras' with which Earthlings make memories that they will also never look at again.

Male and female Earthlings called 'husbands' and 'wives' promise to stay living together forever. The female often seems to wear a long white bedclothing with smaller females attached to it called 'bridesmaids' or tiny cross-looking males called 'pages' (NB, nothing to do with books). The big male is a 'groom' (NB, nothing to do with the person who sweeps up the poo poo of horses). After the promising, guests drone speeches, swig alcohol and make toast for the 'happy couple'.

When the 'happy couple' do their promising, they say 'I do'.
But maybe they should say 'Do I?'

It is quite rare for males to marry males or for females to marry females which is why Earthlings never have six daddies as we often do.

If the happy couple do not like each other later, they are

allowed to 'divorce' which makes everybody cry H_2O from their eyeballs until they get married again to other people and everybody then cries H_2O again about how amazing and wonderful it all is.

If parents divorce, sometimes their younglings hardly see them ever again. Imagine! If one of my mummies stopped liking one of my daddies, she would still like another and we would all be friends.

⭐ **TIP:** Do not mistake a wedding for a joke.

You might not believe this, but Earthling younglings have to be taught how to count! Worse, they use their flimsy gripper digits to do this, limiting themselves to multiplications of ten. They do not move on to calculus, vector theory or differential equations until 'secondary school' (the equivalent of our nurseries). So be warned, maths is the lesson in which you are most likely to reveal yourself as an alien because it is so easy.

Learn from my mistakes. When my teacher, Miss Barn, asked if I knew my nine times table, I lied saying, 'I only know up to two million and six times nine.' She gave me a strange look. Then I made a simple six-dimensional cube, a few flying ozoids and a couple of octagonal pyramids. Everyone crowded round but luckily my hypermood evaluator warned me the general level of amazement was higher than it should be, so I crumpled my designs before Miss Barn could start saying I was a genius.

Interestingly, the Riemann hypothesis still remains unsolved on Earth, though it is clearly identical to Toonfloot's theorem, which Faa mathematicians proved in the Fourth Quadratic period. That's how stupid Earthlings are at maths.

MIRRORS

Earthling adults spend more time in front of mirrors watching themselves than they spend eating or chatting. I have no idea why, considering how ugly they are.

On my second visit to Earth, we attempted to take advantage of Earthlings' vanity by promising to Improve them – offering better hairstyles, muscles, etc and they all ran inside our Improver hoping to come out 'beautiful.' And they did! They had some heads coming out of their elbows and beaks on their feet.

TIP: Earthling adults will often ignore you to check themselves in mirrors, making 'kissy' shapes with their lips, flicking their hairstyles or pulling in their stomachs. Be patient – it is normal Earthling behaviour.

MONEY...

More important than anything else on Earth. Money is made of round flat 'coins', flimsy paper 'notes' and plastic cards. To get what you want on Earth, you do not have to be clever, you just have to be rich. So instead of performing experiments, lassoing moons, understanding why time bends or capturing those dear little particles that create mass as we have to do at home, we can just forge money on Earth.

Most Earthlings have to work for money. Earthling parents are allowed to give their money to their younglings so if your parents are kings, then you can be rich without doing anything at all! Sometimes you will see an Earthling on the pavement holding out their gripper, with a

'Money'
Earthlings love this best of all.

dog on a piece of string and a notice saying, *Workless, please help* or *Helpless, please work*. These are 'beggars' who adults hate. If you wish to help them, do not draw attention to yourself by giving them thousands of your forged pounds – a hundred is enough to make them happy.

Adults prefer to give their money to banks rather than beggars, but banks often spend it badly so there is none left. Younglings are more sensible and keep their money in little china piggies or pockets, which don't spend it. This is called 'pocket money' and is spent on sweeties and 'gum' for sticking in cheeks and decorating streets with.

Charities are there to make Earthlings feel better and it is polite to give money to them. On 'Red Beak Day' Earthlings raise money by shaving their hairstyles, selling broken toys or hopping backwards. I just forged a little extra to put into 'charity tins'.

⭐ **TIP:** Only forge enough money for your daily needs so you're less likely to be caught.

King Kong

M⊕NSTeRS

Susan's eyeballs widened when I ask her where I could find the lunchpack of Notre Dame and other monsters. I think she may be scared of them. I am hoping one day to return to Earth and find these.

Dragon

Cycle-clips*

139

*Editor's note:
Sorry, that should be 'cyclops'.

MUSIC

Now this is something worth hearing about. It is, without doubt, the greatest invention on Earth and one of the truly great things in existence in all the galaxies. It is why we must preserve Earth and respect it as part of the great bio-diversity of the multiverse (as Papa likes to remind me). Your ear trumpets will have heard nothing like it before.

Music is a range of differently pitched noises, high, low, medium, some short and soft, some long and explosive, then short loud sounds and long rippling quiet sounds, all of them vibrating in rapid succession. But this description doesn't begin to do it justice, because each of the sounds flows into the next as though the sound itself is looping. The individual sounds are called 'notes' and when blended together, they are called 'music'.

The first time I heard these sequences, my ear trumpets

tingled and my heads spun round and shot out of my vest. so I had to swallow a whole jug of *Vom*. Now whenever I hear it, whatever kind it is, I tune my ear trumpets to full volume and it feels like flying, zooming, eating chocolate and playing *fatool* at the same time.

Roddy and Susan even made some extra bits of it on music furnitures called 'piano' and 'flute'. Miss Barn said they are 'gifted and talented' which usually means someone can read a whole book or do very simple equations, but for once I agreed with her.

When Susan sang a 'song' (talking with music) I was so excited I had to swig *Vom* again.

No famous Earth musicians are, in fact, from Zargon, despite rumours to the contrary. Oddly, Zargons have never brought music back from Earth (are they mad? Are they tone deaf?) and my own attempt failed when the data storage device I thought was packed with recordings of wonderful music turned out to be blank thanks to Papa's hopeless Earth laptop. If there is one reason to go back to

Earth, it is to collect music and spread it throughout the multiverse.

Also music keeps the dangerous Threggs away. Or I hope so. Recently, this worrying message was intercepted, which suggests the Threggs have found a way to make sure they can't hear the music.

HAR HAR HOO HOR. WE HAVE DEVELOPED SONIC EAR MUFFS! WE WILL INVADE EARTH THIS VERY YEAR AND ELIMINATE MUSIC FROM THE ENTIRE LOONYVERSE. AND THEN, THE EMPIRE OF ETERNAL SPINACH SHALL REIGN SUPREME.

Nincompoop

An excellent Earth word and one of the few that sounds like our own lovely language – but it unfortunately means twit. (Other pleasant words include buffoon, bamboozle, sesquipedalian, curmudgeon, persnickety, profiteroles, and supercalifragilisticexpialidocious. But weirdly, in English no word has more than 45 letters).

Nodding

This is when you move your single head up and down. It usually means 'Yes'. But beware – in one or two countries, it can mean 'No'.

NOXIOUS NOISES

There are a few different causes of these on Earth. Farting is called a 'bottom cough' by teachers. I regret to say it is the passing of a noxious mixture of nitrogen and CO_2 from an Earthling's bottom. The smell is overwhelmingly nauseating, which is why I had to wear my invisible beak muffler for most of my stay on Earth. Younglings, unfortunately, think farting is a huge 'joke'. I still haven't had the hearts to tell my sister Farteeta what her Earth name really means.

Burping (also called belching) is another repellent affliction caused by swallowing

BELCH

air, especially when eating sweeties or fizzy drinks, and subsequently expelling a mixture of nitrogen and oxygen through the mouth. The revolting sound is caused by the vibration of the Earthling's weak upper head tube sphincter.

Hiccups is a distressing condition produced by a sudden convulsion of the puny Earthling diaphragm and consist of abruptly blocked intakes of air, giving rise to a sound somewhat like a *fluit* gurgling lava. Like burping, it may be triggered by overeating or fizzy drinks, but can go on for hours or even days.

Earth doctors are too weedy to cure these ridiculous hiccups but Earthlings use various remedies, the common feature of which is increasing carbon dioxide levels by interrupting breathing: for instance drinking a large glass of H_2O backwards, or holding the breath. A sudden shock is often the only cure.

⭐ **TIP:** If you encounter an Earthling with a fit of the hiccups, display all your heads. That should do the trick. (NB: If revealing yourself to an Earthling, be sure you have your memory blaster ready.)

Oceans + Seas

These masses of H_2O cover 71 per cent of the Earth's surface, leaving only 29 per cent for Earthlings and land animals to live on. No wonder Earth's overpopulated.

If only lovely scaly fish were the dominant species on Earth.

There are five oceans: Pacific, Atlantic (North and South), Arctic, Indian and Southern, but younglings can only name two or three out of five, so make sure you do not tell your teacher all of them.

Earthlings are fond of their oceans, even if they have never travelled to the deepest depths of them. They like to swim in them (only occasionally getting eaten by sharks, or stung to death by stingrays), but they cannot stay underwater for long as they have no gills and would drown.

Fish, however, *can* live in water and like it. And so do octopi, (delightful creatures with eight tentacles like our own), charming jellyfish (do not mistake them for party food), and dear little barnacles and anemones.

I have not yet seen one of the most interesting sea creatures - a mermaid - which is half lady, half fish.

PARTIES

Earthlings are always trying to cheer their dull lives, and often give 'parties' to which they invite other Earthlings. They use any excuse to have one.

Younglings especially like to have parties for birthdays where they must play games like 'throw the teabag' and 'scoff cake till you are sick'.

Adults usually have parties where they drink alcohol, wobble around or fall over, grasp each other closely, and make promises to meet again which they then forget. English Earthlings gave 'The Queen' an enormous party for her jubbly (60 years since her carnation).

TIP: To Improve Earthlings, 'throw a party'. You don't hurl cake at everyone, but you do invite them to your house, where you can lure them into your Improver.

PETS

Any other animal species that Earthlings capture and keep locked in their dwellings. They claim they do this because they love them. Earthlings like their pet creatures more than their younglings.

The most popular Earth pets are revolting, smelly slobbery dogs which cough all the time even when they are not ill. It is called 'barking' which, like 'bats' is a word meaning 'mad'. Dogs can be poodles, noodles, bloodhounds, mudhounds, dalmatians, alsatians and liquorice allsorts.

DOGS MUST BE CARRIED

DOGS MUST BE KEPT ON A LEAD

There are places where you <u>must</u> have a dog. Borrow one whenever you see these signs.

Haughty cats, which poo politely outside their homes (unlike Earthlings), are also popular. Cats can be persian, nasturtium, siamese, burmese, mog or bog.

Younglings also keep hamsters (furballs in wheels), gerbils and goldfish. Unfortunately, before we discovered about fish, Farteeta rescued a goldfish from what we thought was a cruel habit of keeping it in freezing water. It did not like being wrapped in a glove and 'saved' and I warn you not to do the same.

Rich Earthlings have horses that they can ride on but do the biggest poo poos of all. Susan loves horses but you can't keep one in an Earthling 'flat' so I gave her a tiny one that I had shrunk with Farteeta's amazing Shrinker. She kept it on

her 'bedside table' and said one lump of sugar lasted it a whole week. She expanded it when she wanted a ride.

Fred

Frog

Dobbin

Cynthia

Earthlings often grow to resemble their pets

My own pet, Pluke, does not find Earthling pets as hideous as we do. In his disguise as an Earth dog, he fell in love with Fi-Fi, next door's revolting poodle, and the result was four puppies, half Earth poodle and half Pluke. They are sweet, with only two heads each, but that is one too many heads for the Earthlings who captured the puppies and put them in a zoo.

One of Pluke's puppies

⭐ **TIP:** Do not reveal your dislike of Earthling pets. Always stroke them with your grippers (try wearing 'gloves') and say, 'What a nice doggy' (unless it is a cat or a hamster).

Philosophers

Earth's serious 'thinkers'. It is so rare for Earthlings to think properly that they have a special word for people who can do it. Most come from Zargon to help Earthlings but unfortunately Earthling philosophers are becoming extinct.

PHONES

Poor Earthlings have no telepathy so are forced to use 'mobile phones' to communicate important things like shopping lists. They talk or 'text' (a crude form of written language) constantly, especially when crossing 'roads'. They have only had these devices for about 20 Earth years so they must have felt very lonely before then. Ancient Earthlings keep their phones only in their dwellings and are almost impossible to communicate with when not at home.

PICNICS

For having food outside. Not recommended.

PIRATES

Robbers who go, 'Yohohoandabottleofrum' and steal from floating dwellings called ships. They have hooks for grippers, parrots for friends and legs made of trees. If you upset a pirate you must walk the plank and be eaten by sharks. They sound like quite entertaining Earthlings to me.

POCKETS

Some pockets are fastened by 'zips' (metal biters to hurt your grippers).

Small bags attached to clothing for keeping keys, money, paperclips, sweeties and fluff. To find something, Earthlings must rummage through 20 pockets because they have several coats and trousers each with multiple pockets. It is no surprise that they lose things so often.

PoETRy

Poetry is like music AND stories, so good for defeating Threggs AND Squelch.

Poems are short stories, which often rhyme and usually sound like music. Anyway, I like poetry.

I wandered lonely as a cloud
That floats on high o'er vales and hills,
When all at once I saw a crowd,
A host, of golden daffodils.

Translation:
'I walked along by myself. I saw a lot of yellow flowers.'

QUESTIONS

Earthlings, especially adults and in particular teachers, are always asking questions. But if you ask *them* questions, they don't know the answer. Make sure you only ask these stupid Earthlings really easy questions, for example:

'Which of the following is a colour: blue or dog?'

Do not ask your teacher the following questions as I did:

'What is the speed of dark?'

'Why isn't phonetic spelt the way it sounds?'

'How many stars are there in the Milky Way?'

'If people from Finland are Finns, people from Scotland are Scots, and people from Poland are Poles, are people from Holland Holes? And are people from Iceland Ices?'

'Why are centipedes called centipedes when they *never* have one hundred legs?'

'Which has the most neck bones – a giraffe or a mouse?'

Queuing

Important Earthling custom, though only observed in some countries, of waiting in a line. You must always join Earthling lines at the back, or you are a 'queue jumper'. This does not mean you have become an item of Earthling clothing, it means no one likes you, although I have noticed Ancient Earthlings complain that everyone does it nowadays. If you are in a non-queuing country, flap your extenders about in all directions to try to get to the front. In this arrangement, everybody does the same, so nobody likes anybody but quickly forgets it.

Queues are confusing as you might want to queue for a bus but instead you find you are queuing for stamps (small sticky squares pasted to slow messages).

Earthlings love car queues called 'traffic jams'. On rare

sunny days, they choose to join car queues for hours. In the back of the car, younglings say, 'Are we there yet?' and in the front adults shout at 'maps'. (Earthlings need maps to tell them how to direct themselves as they have limited visual spatial awareness and almost NO memory. Some have primitive electronic speaking-maps called satnavs, which direct them into ponds but are not advanced enough to then say, 'You are drowning'.)

Quidditch

Magnificent Earth game, which sounds nearly as exciting as our own *fatool* in which Earthlings somehow manage to make their household brooms fly. I begged Susan to take me to see a Quidditch match but she just gave me an odd look.

RACE

People from different countries are sometimes known as different 'races', which also confusingly means running about. Some people don't like others because they have slightly darker or lighter skin shades although it is impossible for me to tell the difference, because Earthlings all look more alike to me even than a flock of their sheeps.

Adolf Hitler, a small, shouting man with a furry lip, thought one kind of Earthling was much better than other kinds, and started a world war. Since it's obvious to anyone with half a *flaaarnn* working that all Earthlings are exactly the same (except for a few tiny differences of shape, size and furriness) and all of them equally ridiculous, this Hitler was clearly completely mad.

RECYCLING

Earthlings don't recycle their rubbish much, so it is up to us to set a good example.

Unravel your 'jumper' to turn it back into a 'sheep'

<u>OR</u>

Glue hairstyle clippings together to make 'wigs' for baldycoots.

Oh, thanks.

Here you are, Grandpa.

ReLigions

There are lots of different religions for Earthling gods, with nice festivals such as the Olympics (for Zeus, I think), Ramadan where you must go very fast, Xmas where you throw presents down chimneys, or Guy Fawkes, Diwali and Hanukkah with 'fireworks' and 'candles'.

Religious festivals are fun but adults often turn religions into wars. They argue and fight over what they believe and what will happen to them after they're dead, for some reason. In the end, they always think their own religion is better than all the others, a bit like with football teams.

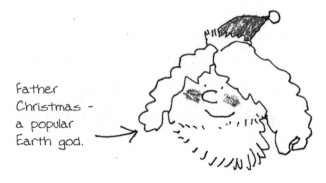

Father
Christmas –
a popular
Earth god.

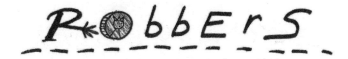

ROBBERS

Robbers take things from other people without asking. In many Earth books, they are described as wearing stripey jumpers and masks and carry sacks with *Swag* written on them, but Susan and Roddy say that robbers look just the same as everyone else until they produce a weapon and point it at you.

Robbers are very popular figures in Earth 'films' and 'stories' which is strange when you consider how much effort Earthlings expend on trying to neutralise them. Maybe most Earthlings would secretly like to be robbers too, so they could collect lots of dwellings, furnitures, cars, paperclips, etc without spending their lives 'working'.

An Earth robber tried to rob me on my way back from school. He put an extender round me as if I was his friend, pulled me into a doorway, and said in my ear, 'Have you got a phone for me?' I said I didn't but he needn't worry because I could tell by telepathy nobody was trying to send a message to him. He thought I was joking and tried to punch my Earth head, but I withdrew it, expanded all my extenders and grippers, turned him upside down and shook him until six phones fell out of his pockets. First he said a lot of rude Earth words, then he started crying. He was not at all like the Earth robbers I had been told about.

☆ **TIP:** Make sure your dwelling burglar alarm is switched on. If a robber comes in, the burglar alarm will be alarmed so you can jump up and say, 'Irish stew in the name of the law'*.

Editor's note: This should be, 'I arrest you in the name of the law,' surely?

Robots

Earth robots are used for dangerous work like bomb disposal, or boring work like vehicle spraying or tiring work like stacking heavy boxes. The Earthlings who are relieved of the dangerous, tiring or boring work that is done by robots are then left to laze around throwing pizza cartons at old ladies. Earth robots cannot solve problems, or dance, or even run up and down stairs but scientists are trying to make them talk and think like humans, which should not be difficult.

Rockets

A thousand years ago in China, the first rockets were built. They were like the 'fireworks' younglings enjoy today. It took ages for Earthlings (with the help, obviously, of Zargons) to develop rockets capable of travelling the 40,000 kilometres per hour necessary to escape Earth's puny gravity, but do not laugh at their rockets as Earthlings are very proud that they have built some that can go into space.

RULERS

Instead of having one Emperor who governs the whole planet as we do (HAIL TO HIS HOLY ROLYPOLINESS!), which would be very sensible, Earthlings have different leaders for every country. And what is more, they change them every few years!

They are kings, prime ministers, presidents, generals, chiefs and princes. In England, they have a female king, called 'The Queen' and when she comes out to play they wave flags and cheer, just like we do for our Emperor, except the Queen is only allowed one husband and she doesn't vaporise anybody. She leaves that to the prime minister.

In many countries Earthlings can choose which brand of ruler they want (in the same way they choose brands of clothes or washing powder or which of many shades of white to paint their dwellings). Susan says this is democracy, the best form of government. She says our obedience to our Emperor means we are frightened.

Which is obviously not true.

HAIL TO HIS HOLY ROLYPOLINESS! HAIL TO THE EMPEROR OF FAA! MAY HE LIVE FOREVER!

Earthlings are too lazy to think of new words so rulers are leaders and measuring sticks.

Sayings

Earthlings often say things that mean something completely different. Here are a few examples that have flummoxed me. I expect you will find others.

'You're getting too big for your boots.'

This does not mean your feet are growing out of your foot covers, but means you are boastful. Earthlings hate pride, perhaps because they have so little to be proud about. You must pretend to be a duffer.

'You have a chip on your shoulder.'

This does not mean part of your upper limb joint is missing or that you have a scorched Earthling potato stuck to it. It means you are envious of people who are better off than you. Why shouldn't you be?

'Keep your hair on.'

It does not mean you are going baldicoot, it means that

you are in danger of losing your Earth 'temper' and must calm yourself.

'Pull your socks up.'

This means 'work hard', so do not worry about your socks falling down even though you will be constantly worried about your socks because they make your Earth feet itch, but it is all part of the burden of pretending to be an Earthling.

'Away with the fairies.'

No, it doesn't mean you have found some fairies, it means you are living in a dream world.

'Smell a rat.'

Does not, alas, mean there is one of these charming rodents in the vicinity, only that there is something not quite right about a situation.

'Put your foot in it.'

Nothing to do with what you might have trodden in, it just means you've done something wrong.

SCARY STUFF

Earthlings are scared of everything so if someone says they have 'agoraphobia' or any other word ending in 'phobia', just nod your head and smile sympathetically. (This means turning up your Earth mouth at both ends in quite a gentle way. Do not give a big 'grin' as they will think you are making fun of them.)

There are millions of stupid things that Earthlings are scared of. A few Earthlings have 'pantophobia', which is not a fear of those Earthling garments 'underpants', but a fear of everything or a fear of nothing, depending which Earth dictionary you use. What weeds they are!

These are some of their most common fears:

Ailurophobia - fear of cats. Cats are either asleep or eating baby birds. The only things that should be scared of them are birds and mice.

Ablutophobia - fear of bathing.
Small Earthlings are scared of falling
down plugholes. They have very little
visio-spatial awareness.

Arachnophobia - fear of spiders.
These are charming eight-legged
creatures who weave webs
stronger than anything else on
earth. Why does anyone find
that scary?

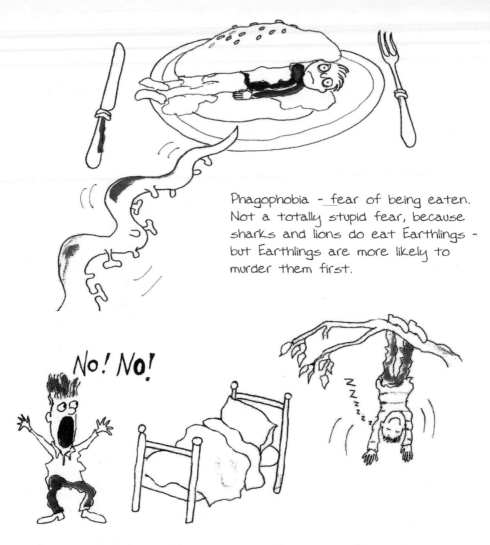

Phagophobia - fear of being eaten. Not a totally stupid fear, because sharks and lions do eat Earthlings - but Earthlings are more likely to murder them first.

No! No!

Clinophobia - fear of going to bed. Since poor Earthlings are forced to go to bed every single night, this must be sad to suffer from. We must teach Earthlings to sleep hanging upside down from a tree.

Oh, dear I have just intercepted a message from some Squelch!

DROOL gloop gurgle

LET THE DROWNING BEGIN!
THE THREGGS HAVE GIVEN
US EARMUFFS SO WE CAN
INVADE THE WET EARTH
PLANET WITHOUT HEARING
THEIR STORIES!

Earthlings are right to worry about bathing after all! Squelch can invade through plugholes! Supposing Keith gives earmuffs to the Wiffly Biffly too, so they can't hear jokes? Then Earth will be doomed.

This is what Earthlings should be really scared of . . .

Should we Faathings try to save them yet again? Is it worth bothering?

SCHOOL

Earthling parents need to go to offices or beg on pavements or visit the hair house or watch TV instead of trying to control their mutinous younglings, so they have built prisons where younglings are forced to read, write and do ludicrously simple sums. This is called 'education' and represents about a sixteenth of the knowledge you and I were born with.

You will have to go to school because it is compulsory in most countries on Earth. Younglings do 'lessons' in classrooms and 'playtime' in 'playgrounds' – concrete rectangles for shouting, skipping and kicking.

Adults moan about how schools are getting worse and no one is learning anything any more but these same adults don't know why most things in the world happen.

But there is a ray of light; Earthling younglings are not so stupid as they appear. Some of them *do* work hard. They may even succeed in teaming up with bats, dolphins and ants to overthrow adults.

⭐ **TIP:** You must write badly, spell worse and forget why time bends to stay disguised at school. I tried to do badly, but Miss Barn put a smiley face on my work anyway.

What to say to your teacher

Good morning, Miss Barn, may I say you look very elegant today?

✓

Could you say that again, Miss Barn? I'm afraid I wasn't listening.

✗

Thank you, Miss Barn, that was a most interesting lesson. I have learnt a lot.

✓

What is the square root of 5698310222?

✗

This is how Earthlings draw stars.

And this is how they draw suns. Don't they realise stars and suns are the same?

Scïence

You will realise by now that Earth science is not worthy of its name. One of their most complicated scientific instruments is the Large Hadron Collider (the sort of thing we make in nursery school), as a result of which their particle physicists have only just claimed to discover the particle that gives things mass (which they rather sweetly call the 'Higgs boson'). Since they are so far behind us in all chemistry, physics and biology, we cannot really converse with them at all on such matters.

TIP: You must be especially careful in school science lessons. On no account try to discuss such subjects as the origin of the symmetry-breaking mechanism by which elementary particles acquire mass, or even the abundance of elements and isotope ratios in solar system objects, such as meteorites. Instead, try saying you believe the sun goes round the Earth, or that a man lives in the moon.

These are supply zones with large portholes where Earthlings buy the things they need like pegs to hang their clothes on, furnitures for brushing their hairstyles and paperclips.

Shopping for dressing up and foot covers is the favourite pastime of many Earthling females. Younglings and Earthling males often refuse to 'go shopping', especially if the Earth mama says, 'Get cow juice for me while you're out.'

Earthlings often have different shops for different things. Do not ask for ice cream in an underpants shop, for instance, chickens in a chemist's, books in a fish shop, and so on.

Earthlings buy more things than they need because of 'advertisements' which make Earthlings think that their kitchens or toys or clothing could be much better. Words like *new*, *free*, *best*, and *healthy* appear a lot in them for things that are old, the same as other things, cost money and are bad for you.

Example of Earth advertisement

DON'T BE FAT
GET MORE THIN
WEAR THIS HAT
BUY THIS TIN!

TIP: Do not take things from Earth shops without paying. This is known as 'shop lifting' and a hairy judge can jail you. If you have forgotten to forge any money, it is best to lift the whole shop and fly off with it.

S L A V E S

We have slaves from nearby planets on Faa, of course, and we're hoping to Improve Earthlings by adding extra intelligence and heads etc, so they can be useful slaves for us too. But we would never dream of treating another Faathing as a slave, whereas on Earth they had human slaves as recently as 150 years ago! These humans were literally the property of their masters and were whipped and chained. We would never do that to our slaves!

You will probably want to catch Earthlings to bring back fo Faa to use as slaves. Invite them to a 'party' at your house and then persuade them into the Improver – tempt younglings with free ice cream, and adults with the promise of looking better or getting rich, and they will happily enter the Improver.

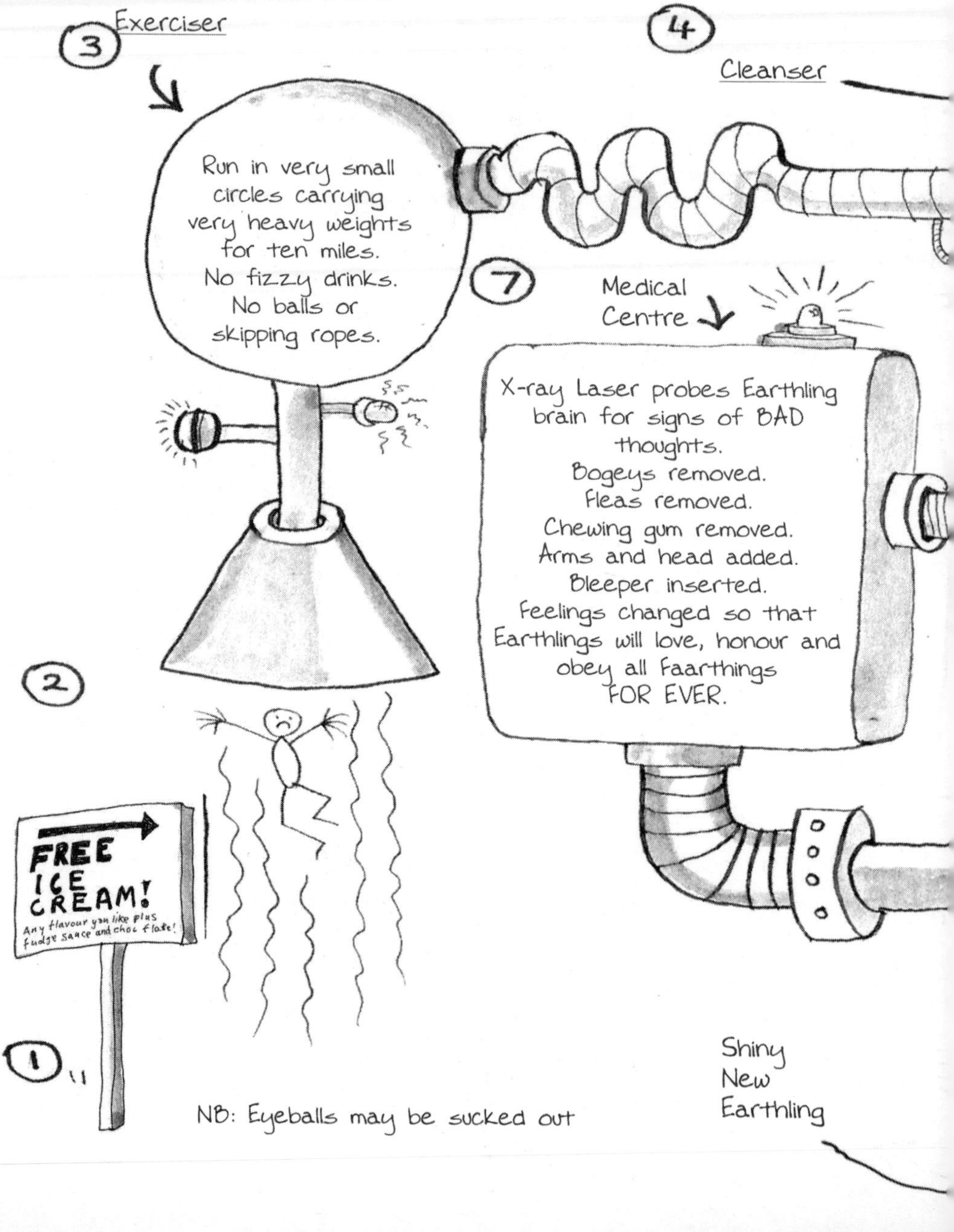

Exerciser
3
Run in very small circles carrying very heavy weights for ten miles. No fizzy drinks. No balls or skipping ropes.
4
Cleanser
7
Medical Centre
X-ray Laser probes Earthling brain for signs of BAD thoughts. Bogeys removed. Fleas removed. Chewing gum removed. Arms and head added. Bleeper inserted. Feelings changed so that Earthlings will love, honour and obey all Faarthings FOR EVER.
2
FREE ICE CREAM!
Any flavour you like plus fudge sauce and choc flake!
1
NB: Eyeballs may be sucked out
Shiny New Earthling

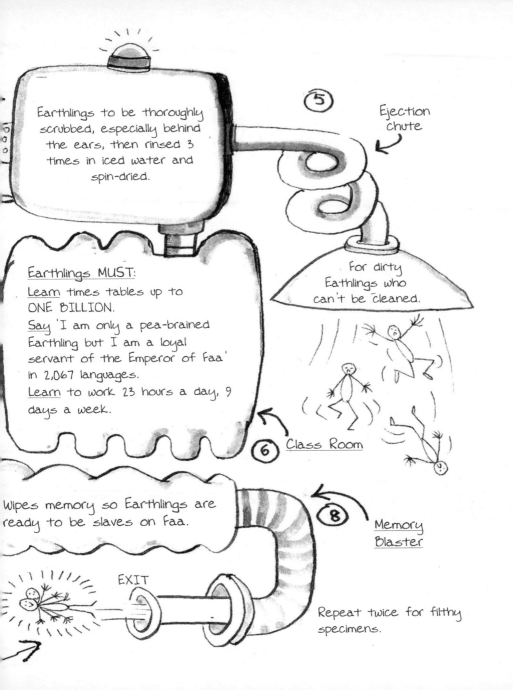

Earthlings to be thoroughly scrubbed, especially behind the ears, then rinsed 3 times in iced water and spin-dried.

⑤ Ejection chute

For dirty Earthlings who can't be cleaned.

Earthlings MUST:

Learn times tables up to ONE BILLION.

Say 'I am only a pea-brained Earthling but I am a loyal servant of the Emperor of Faa' in 2,067 languages.

Learn to work 23 hours a day, 9 days a week.

⑥ Class Room

Wipes memory so Earthlings are ready to be slaves on Faa.

⑧ Memory Blaster

EXIT

Repeat twice for filthy specimens.

SMELLS

You should wear your invisible beak muffler throughout your Earth stay, as I'm afraid the pong is unspeakable. Or rather, unsmellable. Earthlings have a very limited range of senses and their olfactory organs (situated inside their bogey-filled beaks) are extremely underdeveloped, so they have no idea how awful they smell to us. As for their pets . . .

⭐ **TIP:** NEVER mention that Earthlings smell. They get offended. Occasionally you might remove the muffler so you can smell a flowering vegetable called a rose, or chocolate. It is tragic when you think that these are the best smells Earthlings experience. They have never sniffed a *lunar tabula*, nor bathed in *ambrosiaosia*.

Smoking / Alcohol

These are quite different, but schools always mention them together for some reason.

We sizzle and smoke when all four of our heads are angry, but I haven't seen anyone on Earth smoking. Susan said smoking is not to do with feelings, but to do with paper tubes full of toxins that Earthlings put in their mouths and set light to – for fun!

Adults like to swig alcohol – a foul-smelling chemical that destroys the few working brain-cells they have. Our neighbour, Mr Snell, often visited alcohol drinking houses and returned home shouting rude words and unable to open his front door. His wife then shouted rude words too, so the effect of alcohol is obviously catching, even if you haven't drunk any.

SOCKS

Infuriating foot covers that must be worn under outer foot covers. Socks are supposed to come in matching 'pairs', but you can make your otherwise gloomy trip on Earthling transport more enjoyable by examining passengers' socks. They will seldom match. This is because even when Earthlings only buy black socks, each sock turns a slightly different texture and colour after it has been washed (to try to rid it of its horrific pong of dried cow juice).

SPACE EXPLORATION

The only other astronomical object apart from Earth in all the galaxies that Earthlings have ever trodden on is their own tiny moon – a dust ball, which they said was a 'giant leap for mankind'. Only twelve Earthlings have ever walked on the moon, and they said the moon's dust feels like snow and smells like gunpowder.

Earthlings think there are only eight planets in their solar system. I made sure I didn't tell my Earthling teacher, Miss Barn, that Faathings have counted two milion planets in Earth's solar system. Earthlings will never discover them unless they learn to see dark matter.

☆ **TIP:** Be excited and admiring if Earthlings talk about their adventures in 'outer space' as they touchingly call it.

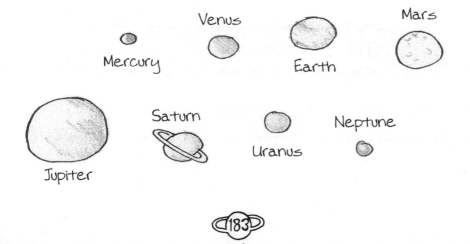

SPINACH

Don't go anywhere near this green vegetable – Threggs love it even more than younglings hate it.

Oh no! We've just intercepted this message:

HOO HOO HAR!
IT IS I, KEITH, KING OF THREGGS, LORD OF THE LOONYVERSE, SPINACH FINDER GENERAL. WE HAVE GIVEN EARMUFFS TO ALL OUR ALLIES AND WILL SOON ANNIHILATE EVERYTHING ON YOUR PUTRID PLANET. EVERYTHING EXCEPT MAGNIFICENT SPINACH.

Oh dear. This is very worrying for Earthlings, but maybe they deserve to be extinguished.

SUPERHEROES

These are men in tights named after superior creatures like bats or spiders. They fly round and solve crimes but again, when I asked to meet one, Susan laughed. Perhaps their activities are so secret, Earthlings are afraid to reveal their whereabouts. I will pursue this mystery and report back. The secrets of superheroes may provide Earthlings with some hope for the future, though I suspect they are from planet Zargon.

I still have not met an Earthling superhero but I would like to.

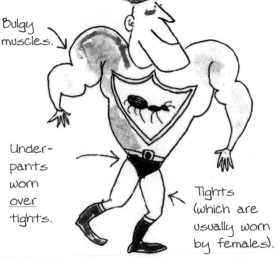

Bulgy muscles.

Under-
pants
worn
over
tights.

Tights
(which are
usually worn
by females).

SWIMMING

Earthlings are so bad at swimming it breaks my hearts. They do pathetic flaps and wiggles called 'crawls' and 'best strokes'. Their absence of gills means they drown easily.

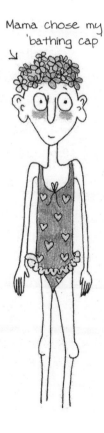

Mama chose my 'bathing cap'

When I first entered Earth water in a 'swimming pool', the cold was so shocking that three of my tentacles shot out. I revolved them as fast as possible to stop them being seen, but it sent me up to the other end of the pool in 5.2 nanoseconds. Luckily Susan brought me some *Vom* before anyone realised what was happening.

⭐ **TIP:** Flap about sadly and ask for a rubber ring if you want to 'fit in'.

To get H_2O, Earthlings must use 'taps' – odd things attached to sinks, basins and baths. I found these difficult to manipulate using my two feeble grippers. Remember the simple rule: turn right to get H_2O and turn left to stop H_2O – righty tighty, lefty loosey.

 TIP: Watch out for the dreaded Squelch who can appear from taps.

Clumsy, spotted Earthlings neither adult nor youngling. When they walk into rooms, things fly about and fall off walls. They leave a clothe trail behind them and are champions at the game called 'losing things'. They are blamed for most of what is wrong with Earthling society, but I like them as they enjoy thinking and have noble ideas, like world peace, and make excellent 'music'.

Tickets

Little slips of paper with which you can gain entry to cinemas, buses, trains and more. They prove an Earthling has paid money for something. As long as you are accompanied to Earth by an efficient robot you will be able to generate your own tickets which are identical to the Earthling originals. You will also make many friends, as tickets are the second most popular thing for Earthlings to lose.

TIME

Earth's surface is divided into 24 'time zones' so it is a different time of day in different countries. They have a 24 hour day, a seven day week, a four week month and a 12 month year. Each hour is divided into 60 minutes and each of those is 60 whole seconds long! A second on Earth feels to us like several hours, since Earthlings' minds and their movements are intolerably sluggish. Even Einstein could barely convince them that time bends. We Faathings sense from the angles of our suns, moons and stars precisely what time of the day or night it is, as well as the galactic date, but Earthlings can't, so use cumbersome methods called 'clocks' or 'watches'.

TIP: If someone asks the time, pretend to look at your 'watch' or check your phone before you tell them.

Toilet

I am sorry to report that Earthlings do poo-poos just like our pets do. But they don't dig a hole outside, they do it in a little furniture called a toilet – INSIDE their own homes! They are so primitive that they don't even digest all the food they eat!

On our first day on Earth, we found Farteeta weeping beside a roaring, gurgling beast. 'I just shook its hand!' she wailed. 'Now it's gushing and spitting at me.'

Papa fired three shots from his stun laser at the brute, which exploded, flooding the room and then Mama looped in screeching, 'You've smashed the toilet!'

☆ **TIP:** Ensure that your dwelling contains one of these furnitures in working order as Earthlings must use them all the time. We did not get the toilet surgeon to fix ours immediately, with embarrassing results.

Younglings need toys to 'play' with. Get some if you are living as a 'family' or Earthlings will think you are 'deprived' and call social services to put you in a prison or zoo.

Adult Earthlings also have toys like TVs, screwdrivers and hairstyle dryers, but they are called 'gadgets'. Males like to cover their toys in dust and rust and keep them in nice 'sheds' in the garden where females don't visit.

☆ **TIP:** Learn to 'bounce' a sphere, brush a dolly's hairstyle and go 'bang bang' with a gun to 'fit in'.

TRANSPORT

Being unable to fly, loop or zoom, Earthlings rely on various means of 'transport' to enable them to move to shopping zones. Unfortunately, unless you travel at night, you will have to use these bumpy, rickety, agonisingly slow transports.

While observing Earth from afar, Faathings once believed 'cars' were the dominant Earth species. Cars travel smoothly in straight lines, live in pleasant accommodation called 'garages' and behave in an orderly way, stopping whenever they see a red light and going when the light turns green.

We thought cars were plagued by unruly parasites, who sucked the life out of them until they stopped and then abandoned them, only returning once their energy had recovered and plaguing them for another long journey.

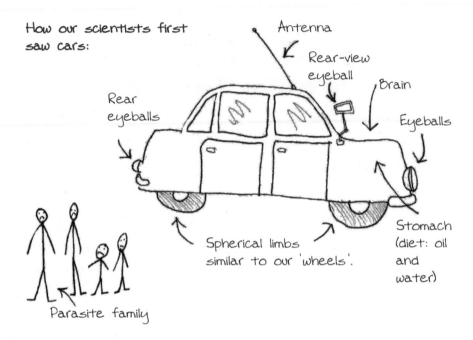

How our scientists first saw cars:

Antenna

Rear-view eyeball

Brain

Rear eyeballs

Eyeballs

Spherical limbs similar to our 'wheels'.

Stomach (diet: oil and water)

Parasite family

Now we know that cars are in fact a means of transport, built and used by the parasites (human beings) to get from one part of Earth to another. For this, they invented wheels which they then attached to longer vehicles called 'buses' and 'trains'. (These shared transports are best avoided if possible as you are squashed uncomfortably close to humans.)

Humans have even built flying machines and space rockets, with help from Zargonites, although they have not visited anywhere except their single tiny moon.

In big cities they must burrow undergound like 'moles' in tube trains, where at least there are names on the stations so they can know where they are, which is not always true of buses.

Water transports include 'Noah's Ark' for pets, 'Jolly Roger' for pirates, 'yachts' for million airs and 'Titanic' for ghosts.

TIP: To use buses or trains you must buy a ticket.

TIP: You will have to endure 'traffic jams' which is not a sugary food, but is one of Earthlings' favourite things to do while sitting in their cars. This habit is known as 'rush hour', though it is very badly named, since it refers to the times of day when everything moves around even more slowly than usual.

TREES

Tiny versions of our own beloved *urqflurbles* that we sleep in, although they are far less chatty and trees mostly stay in one place. Younglings love to swing, fall out of, and build houses in them. Revolting dogs like to do wees on them.

Without trees, Earth would be dead, as, like all green vegetables, they absorb CO_2 and release oxygen.

THE LAST
TREE ON
EARTH

Earth vegetables have an unfortunate tendency to make puns.

'Forests', which are large gatherings of trees, also prevent floods and provide firewood, paper, outlaws, merry men, planks for building, witches, giants, gingerbead houses, oils and medicines. Some Earth scientists think half of all forests will have disappeared by the year 2020.

⭐ **TIP:** Use your inter-species translator to talk to trees. I think they know more than they are letting on.

Frankly it's been downhill for me since the Bible. The first years were good, but all that stuff about Adam and Eve got me down. Gave me the pip. Bored me to the core.

A flat screen in two dimensions, so how could it tell you anything worth knowing? Papa banned us from watching TV for most of our Earth visits, saying it would radiate our delicate Faa brains. Most Earthlings are glued to it (which means, literally stuck) for many months each year.

UMBRELLA

Despite their appalling weather conditions, Earthlings have not built any satisfactory defences. Umbrellas are meant to act as rain protectors, but are also for blowing inside out, trapping grippers in their springs and getting left behind on transports. As a result, Earthlings buy on average 57 umbrellas each, but do not own any. They are the top things for Earthlings to lose. Sensible younglings rarely bother with them.

UNICORN

Half horse, half rhino. They are very shy so are not in any zoos.

VALENTINES

In the Earth month of February, teenage and adult Earthlings have a special day where they kiss each other and send little paper rectangles covered in 'hearts'.

This is how Earthlings like to draw hearts. If you send a real heart in an envelope, they get upset. The messages say things like:

TO MY ONE AND ONLY
HUGGY BUNNY.

So now you can see why Earthling adults are not very grown up.

At my school some of the younglings got Valentine cards but most of us didn't. If you get one, everybody goes 'Ooooh' or 'Yuck'. So I am not sure if it is a good thing or not.

VAMPIRES

I am hoping to discuss the finer qualities of the bat kingdom with the Count Dracula on my next visit.

Half human, half bat, the king of vampires is Count Dracula who was born in Transylvania in 1471. He is still alive, being one of the great 'undead' and comes out at night to drink Earthling blood. Vampires sleep in houses for dead Earthlings called coffins. I am keen to capture a vampire.

vegetables

Vegetables are plants – eg: grass, trees, carrots, tulips, onions. There are many different types of vegetables. My personal favourite was the pretty venus fly trap until I discovered it eats delightful flies!

Many vegetables, including the 'fruits' which they produce, form part of the human diet and teachers say they are very good for younglings, although most humans, including teachers, prefer to eat pets with ice cream.

I am suggesting that our Improver be adapted to help humans digest Earth's most plentiful vegetable – grass – so that no humans will starve. However, if we succeeded, perhaps grass would soon cost loads of Earth money and be in 'recipe' books, being called things like 'Meadow Marinade' or 'Grass Goulash'.

If Earthlings ate more leaves and carrots and cucumbers
~~and spinach~~ (whoops, watch out for Threggs)
they would live longer.

VIOLENCE

Earthlings' favourite hobby, which includes boxing, biffing and bashing. When not being violent they are watching violence on their TVs or playing it on computer games.

 TIP: Join in whenever you can or you will be seen as weedy. Your school playground will offer lots of opportunities to practise. However, be careful not to show additional extenders or grippers if you use them. It is easy to defeat even the most violent Earthlings by simple extender-manouevres performed too quickly for their limited Earthling vision to observe. Releasing the belts of opponents to lower their trousers, tying their shoelacys together or emptying their lunchboxes into their underpants are all useful tactics.

WEATHER

Earthlings have no idea that 'weather' is different from 'climate'. As you and I know, weather changes every day but climate is the pattern of weather over a long time. So when it is freezing cold, Earthlings say there is no such thing as global warming. But of course there is, and it is putting their planet in danger.

England's weather goes like this:

Spring   Summer   Autumn   Winter

There are four seasons, which you can easily spot by watching 'leaves', which are little vegetables growing on the bigger vegetables called 'trees'.

Spring: The leaves are beginning to grow. Vegetables called 'flowers' appear and birds hatch out of eggs to get eaten by pet cats. In spring, it is mostly raining.

Summer: Leaves are big and green, trees look happy. Summer is sometimes warmer than spring. In summer, it mostly rains, but if it doesn't for a few days there is a thing called 'drought' where you must turn off your taps.

Autumn: The leaves turn brown and fall off. Earth poets call the leaves 'golden', but then they also think the Earth sun is bright. Younglings jump about in crackly autumn leaves treading in dog poo poo which sticks to their shoe and comes into school. In autumn, the weather is mainly rain.

Winter: In this season you get freezing snowballs falling from space. Younglings throw these freezing blobs at their friends for fun and make them into sculptures. Do not be scared of white giants on winter streets wearing sinister hats and necklaces made of old sheeps. They are only a kind of snow sculpture called 'snowmen'.

In winter, if it isn't snowing, it is mainly raining.

You must take an interest in the weather, otherwise you will not be able to partake in Earthling conversations like this:

Don't worry about these sinister looking creatures.

'LOVELY day for the time of year.'

'Yes, but it's bound to cloud over soon.'

Most Earthlings are pessimistic in this way.

NB: Be on constant lookout for the dreaded Squelch, who are always looking for wet planets to take over.

dribble

whoopee cushion

Small rubber inflatables that emit farting sound when sat on. These are important jokes. (Sorry, but this is the kind of thing Earthlings find amusing.)

⭐ **TIP:** Carry one to make friends and repel Wiffly Biffly.

WITCHES

Earthlings with pointy hats, who can do magic and can fly on sticks. Other Earthlings used to cook them on fires, so now they are all in hiding.

Younglings enjoy dressing up as witches during Hallo Ian as peculiarly, Earthlings find them scary. I think I would like them very much however, as they are fond of frogs, toads, bats and spiders and are best friends with the highly intelligent Earth boy Harry Potter. They are also excellent at spelling.

Earthlings say witches are 'ugly' and film stars are 'beautiful' but I think witches are nicer.

"WORRYING"

A habit like stress, mainly done by mamas. We usually leave worrying to our worried head, but poor Earthlings have only one head and it can spend all day, even all year, worrying about jobs and hairstyles and money. They should be worrying about global warming and Threggs.

XMAS

About 33 per cent of Earthlings celebrate Xmas, also called Christmas. Younglings worship an ancient, fat, bearded man who lives in the sky and is called 'Father Christmas' or 'Santa'. He finds out who is naughty or nice and if they are nice he goes, 'Ho ho ho,' and throws presents down their chimney. There are some nice younglings at my school who do not get presents from Santa and some nasty ones who do. I have been trying to discover why this is.

When Papa heard about someone coming from the sky saying, 'Ho ho ho,' he thought it was a Thregg. I told him, 'That's not Keith, King of Threggs, going, "Hoo hoo har,", it's Father Christmas going, "Ho ho ho!"'

English Earthlings also worship a large vegetable called a 'Christmas Tree'. They drag it from its forest home, squash it inside their dwellings, then disguise it with light bulbs so that other trees won't be able to rescue it.

On 'Christmas Day' which is December 25, Earthlings give everyone in their family 'presents'. These presents are smothered in layers of paper for Earthlings to tear off. Then they must shout, 'Hooray! Just what I wanted.' If they go, 'Oh no, I don't like it', they are being rude.

Mama got our Christmas tree from the garden and hung shiny pots and cutlery on it. I think she did a fine job.

For feeding, they burn a noble creature called 'Turkey' and set fire to a pudding.

'Mistletoe' is not missing toes. It is a vegetable that hangs about and has to endure Earthlings kissing beneath it.

Some Earthlings explode sticks called 'crackers' filled with tiny paper head covers and 'jokes'. These say things like:

What do you call a man with brown paper trousers?

Russell

or

What's furry and minty?

A polo bear

I still have trouble understanding 'jokes'.

At school, we sang songs called 'carols' about Father Christmas being weighed in a manger and bringing peas on Earth and good swill to all men.

Everyone says, 'Happy Christmas,' and turns their Earthling mouths up in a friendly smile. After Christmas you must say 'Happy New Ear'.

Instead of a star, you can murder a large insect called a 'fairy' and stick that on the top of your Christmas tree.

Christmas fairies carry weapons called 'wands'.

XXXXXXX

A symbol for the floppy wet soppy pastime, kissing. But it is also the symbol for 'wrong'.

X-RAY

When Earthlings break part of their flimsy 'skeleton', doctors make them transparent with X-ray machines. Of course, we have X-ray vision so have no need of them.

TIP: Avoid Earthling X-rays at all costs. Otherwise a doctor might see all your hearts and lungs and discover your alien identity.

Younglings

Young Earthlings (also known as 'children') are, frankly, nincompoops. They are without discipline or knowledge. They cannot even read simple words until they are about six years old, and then only books about quackers or bears.

Younglings' fascination with quackers is the subject of an essay by King Snortveltdter from the planet Thwang. I do not recommend your reading it, as it is 70 million pages long and concludes that quackers should be used only as 'toys' in Earth baths. Bears, however, are one of the most dangerous species on Earth and would kill you as soon as look at you, yet younglings take toy bears to bed to cuddle at night. This would be like one of us cuddling a toy Thregg.

ZOO

Museum for living creatures. I was hoping to see some Earthlings in the zoo, to learn about their funny ways. But of course they only lock other creatures up.

Sponge - must be used in bath with slippy soap, floaty duck etc. On what other planet do inhabitants clean themselves with a CREATURE?

Crab: Lovable crustacean who, with a few more heads, would look very like our Emperor's favourite wife. HAIL TO THE EMPEROR! MAY HE LIVE FOREVER.

Lion - they spend 20 hours of the 24 earth day resting, very like Earth film stars. This picture is of my friend Darren, who hated being callled Simba by the zoo keeper.

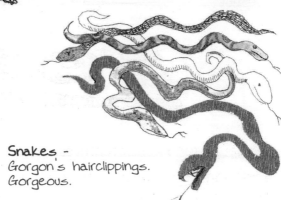

Snakes - Gorgon's hairclippings. Gorgeous.

Giraffe - Nearly as tall as us faathings, with pleasant dapples and delightful purple tongues covered in attractive bristles.

Tortoise - Very thoughtful animal, recognised by Zargon visitors as a philosopher. Can get to places quicker than a rabbit.

Jellyfish - Transparent sea floaters. It is true that they are without hearts, brains or blood, that they are cannibals and have stings that can kill - but most of them are harmless, they provide shelter to little crabs and are used as medicines. So, like most things in the universe, they have a good side and a bad side.

You can add Earth items, habits, oddities or
anything I have left out.

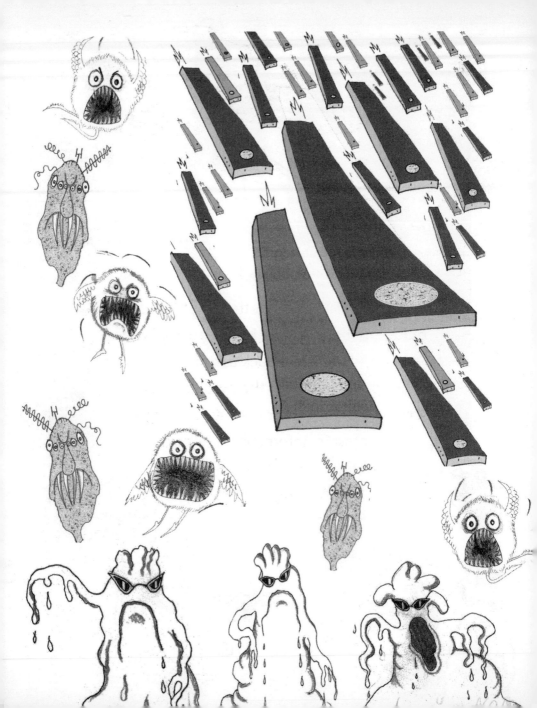

Oh no!

Maybe you will never get the time to use this
guide – it looks like the baddies are joining
forces to attack Earth!
Visit quickly, or keep the eyes of all four
of your heads peeled for my future intergalactic
messages for infomation on the fate
of this miserable, moany but
fascinating planet . . .

For out of this world activities,
a Faathing guide,
and to read Flowkwee's
galactic blog,
go to:

alienschoolboy.co.uk